S320
Science: Level 3

The Open University

Infectious disease

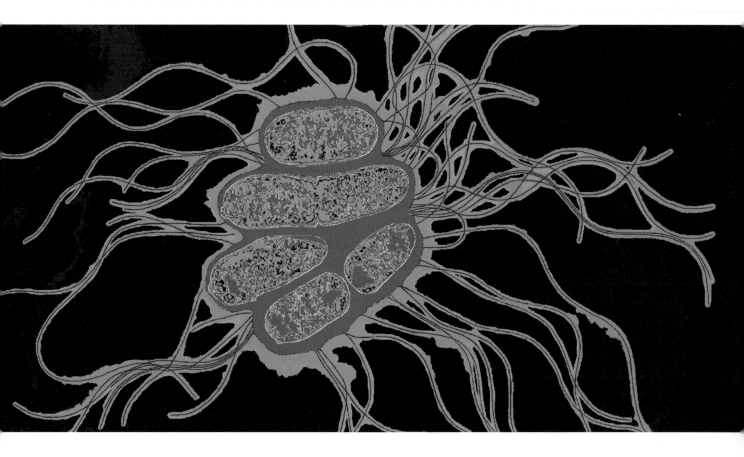

Book 2 Infectious Agents

Prepared for the Course Team by Laura Hibberts,
Eric Bowers and Hilary MacQueen

This publication forms part of an Open University course S320 *Infectious disease*. The complete list of texts which make up this course can be found at the back. Details of this and other Open University courses can be obtained from the Student Registration and Enquiry Service, The Open University, PO Box 197, Milton Keynes MK7 6BJ, United Kingdom: tel. +44 (0)845 300 60 90, email general-enquiries@open.ac.uk

Alternatively, you may visit the Open University website at http://www.open.ac.uk where you can learn more about the wide range of courses and packs offered at all levels by The Open University.

To purchase a selection of Open University course materials visit http://www.ouw.co.uk, or contact Open University Worldwide, Walton Hall, Milton Keynes MK7 6AA, United Kingdom for a brochure. tel. +44 (0)1908 858793; fax +44 (0)1908 858787; email ouw-customer-services@open.ac.uk

The Open University
Walton Hall, Milton Keynes
MK7 6AA

First published 2003. Reprinted 2004 (with corrections) and 2007

Edited and designed by The Open University.

Typeset by The Open University.

Printed and bound in the United Kingdom by The University Press, Cambridge.

ISBN 978 0 7492 5653 1

1.3

THE S320 COURSE TEAM

CONTENTS

1 INTRODUCTION

Any organism or material that causes a disease may be referred to as a pathogen, from the Greek *pathos*, meaning pain or suffering. The subject of this book is **pathobiology**, the study of biological agents that cause disease. Since this is a course about infectious disease, our interests here will be confined to those agents that cause infectious disease. Infectious agents form one of the most diverse groups you will ever come across. They include members of the bacteria, viruses, prions and fungi, conventionally known as pathogens, and those protoctists and invertebrates usually referred to as parasites. A summary of the characteristics of the groups to which infectious agents belong is given in Table 1.1 (overleaf), along with the chapter in which they are discussed.

> If you have not studied *Biology: Uniformity and Diversity* (S204) and are not familiar with the groups listed in Table 1.1, then you will need to devote some time to the S204 Book 4 material on the Reference CD as you work through this book. If you come across an unfamiliar technical term that is not explained here, look for an explanation in the reference material.

From Table 1.1 you can glimpse the astonishing variety that exists among biological agents of infectious disease, which range in size from single molecules of protein to intestinal worms several metres long, and include subcellular particles, prokaryotes and eukaryotes. Some of these agents have special structures that allow them to persist in the external environment, and whilst these structures are not necessary for persistence in the human body, they may help the pathogen to move from one host to another.

We start our study of pathobiology with a historical introduction to the subject. We then go on to look at how the various infectious agents have become adapted to their mode of life, and to consider how they may move from one host to another. Then in the main body of the book we will look at each type of infectious agent in turn and, using selected diseases as examples, examine how they interact with humans to cause illness. In other words, we will be examining the **pathology** of the various biological agents of infectious disease. While you are studying this course, it should occur to you that people in developing countries suffer a disproportionate amount of mortality (death) and morbidity (illness) as a result of infectious disease. You might like to consider whether this is acceptable, and if not, what can be done about it.

Some biological agents of disease, such as the subcutaneous guinea worm (see Chapter 7), are easily seen with the unaided eye and have been known since ancient times. Parasites like these, and other invertebrate parasites such as insects, were easy to identify as agents of disease because they could be easily observed. However, the majority of agents remained undiscovered for centuries after the diseases that they cause were first described, since they were invisible to the naked eye. Hieronymus Fracastorius was centuries ahead of his time when, in 1546, he suggested that small particles were the infectious agents of disease. However, it was not until microscopes were invented, in the 17th century, that the microscopic world could be glimpsed.

TABLE 1.1 Summary of the main characteristics of the different groups in which human infectious agents are found.

Type of biological agent and where they are discussed in this book	Structure	Size range	Reproduction	Specialized persistence structures
bacteria (Chapter 2)	prokaryotes	typically 1–2 μm* in diameter and 2–5 μm long	mainly by binary fission, but sexual reproduction may occur by conjugation	bacterial spores
viruses (Chapter 3)	subcellular particles	10–400 nm* in diameter	replication occurs by the assembly of pre-formed components	no, but the basic structures of some viruses allow them to persist in the environment
prions (Chapter 4)	infectious proteins	relative molecular mass (M_r) 33 000–35 000	replicate by converting normal proteins to prion conformation	none
protoctists (Chapter 5)	unicellular and multicellular eukaryotes	range from microscopic single-celled organisms to sea kelps 60 m long†	most reproduce both sexually and asexually, but some reproduce only asexually	cysts
fungi (Chapter 6)	unicellular and coenocytic eukaryotes	range from microscopic unicellular yeasts to macroscopic mould structures, e.g. 'fairy rings' whose size may be in metres†	all reproduce asexually, and most can reproduce sexually; reproduction usually produces spores, but yeasts may reproduce asexually by budding or fission	fungal spores
invertebrate parasites (Chapter 7)	multicellular eukaryotes			
helminths		adults range from a few mm to several metres in length; larval stages are often a few hundred μm long	many reproduce both sexually and asexually, depending on life cycle stage others reproduce only sexually	cysts or eggs in some species, but many transferred via an intermediate host or vector
arthropods‡		range from a few mm to several cm	sexual reproduction	none

* The abbreviation 'μm' means micrometre, i.e. 10^{-6} m; similarly, 'nm' means nanometre, 10^{-9} m.

† Sea kelps and the fungi that form fairy rings are *not* among the infectious species.

‡ Invertebrate arthropod parasites (e.g. lice, ticks) are not discussed in this book.

Anton van Leeuwenhoek is credited with the discovery of microbes in 1676. He named the strange creatures he saw down his microscope 'animalcules', and it has been speculated that they were the protoctist parasite *Giardia lamblia*, which causes diarrhoeal disease in humans. Despite the discovery of these microscopic creatures, microbes were not linked with diseases until two centuries later. The idea that some microbes might be responsible for diseases was called the 'germ theory' of disease. It seems incredible to us now, but acceptance of the germ theory was delayed by the rival theory of spontaneous generation. This theory held that life could be generated spontaneously from non-living matter, and was supported by observations such as rotten meat 'spontaneously' producing maggots. Of course, we know now that these maggots arise from eggs laid by flies, and are not generated spontaneously at all!

The germ theory of disease was finally accepted in about 1900, largely as a result of Robert Koch's work on *Bacillus anthracis*, the bacterium that causes anthrax. Robert Koch, a German doctor, used a series of experiments to demonstrate unequivocally that *Bacillus anthracis* was the causative agent of anthrax. The criteria he used to prove the relationship between the bacterium and the disease became known as Koch's postulates (described in the Influenza Case Study, Book 1), and have been used as a 'gold standard' when establishing whether an organism causes a particular disease. Koch himself became one of the founding fathers of the new science of microbiology. There followed a so-called 'golden age' of around 50 years, when many of the major human bacterial, fungal, protoctist and helminth agents of disease were identified, or linked to a specific disease. The grand finale of this period was the discovery of viruses, although no-one actually saw a virus until several decades later, after the electron microscope had been invented. Prions, the causative agents of spongiform encephalopathies, such as bovine spongiform encephalopathy (BSE), have been recognized only in the last few decades and are still controversial as agents of disease.

○ Using Koch's postulates as the test, suggest one reason why the controversy over prions exists.

● The main reason is that since they are protein molecules and have no nucleic acid, prions cannot be 'grown' in pure culture, so cannot fulfil Koch's second postulate.

1.1 Parasitism as a way of life

The human body offers a rich variety of habitats for parasites. In this section, the term parasite is used in its widest context, since the vast majority of infectious agents are parasites too. Parasites found on the external surfaces of the body are termed **ectoparasites**, while those found within the tissues are known as **endoparasites**. Endoparasites differ in their degree of penetration: some remain in the outer layers of tissues, while others penetrate deep into the body, and the most extreme endoparasites, such as viruses, actually live inside the host's cells.

○ Can you suggest what criteria have to be met by a successful parasite?

● A successful parasite has to satisfy a number of criteria. It must be able to attach itself to a host, and either remain on the exterior and spread locally, or enter the host's body. If it does enter the host's body, spreading either locally or systemically (i.e. throughout the whole body), it must reproduce and let progeny exit the body where they may find a new host. This must all be accomplished while evading the host's immune response and other defences against infection.

The processes of parasite invasion, proliferation and release of progeny often result in tissue damage to the host, manifested as symptoms of disease. All successful pathogens are able to breach the defences of a healthy host. Organisms that can only cause disease in an individual whose defences have been compromised in some way – for example, by injury, drugs or another disease – are called opportunistic pathogens. The degree of damage actually caused to the host varies widely. Some parasites produce almost no detectable damage, while others may kill the host in a matter of days. The severity of a disease can often be linked to the ease with which the parasite may be spread from one host to another. If spread requires close contact, as is the case for cold viruses, then the disease produced is likely to be mild.

○ Can you suggest what advantage there is to the cold virus in causing only a mild disease?

● A mild disease is unlikely to immobilize the host. For the virus to spread, the host must be well enough to mix with potential new hosts.

If, on the other hand, an incapacitated host can easily spread an organism to new hosts, for example by contaminating the water supply with infected diarrhoea, or by being bitten by a mosquito (as occurs during the spread of malaria; see Book 1, Malaria Case Study), then the disease produced is likely to be more severe. Often the symptoms produced by a parasite are simply a consequence of its presence, but sometimes they are of direct benefit to the organism. For example, infection with the *Vibrio cholerae* bacterium results in the severe diarrhoea of cholera. This diarrhoea provides an excellent way for the bacterium to get into the water supply and infect new hosts.

1.2 Adaptations to parasitism

As a group, parasites exhibit a number of characteristics that allow them to meet the demands of their way of life. They may show degeneration, that is, the loss of unused structures; for example, many parasitic invertebrates have no sense organs. Parasites often have penetrative devices for gaining access to the host, such as the mouthparts of many insects that pierce human skin. Attachment devices, such as the microscopic hair-like structures on bacteria known as **pili**, are often crucial to a parasite. Some infectious agents, mainly bacteria, produce toxins. These toxins are often responsible for some or all of the symptoms of a particular disease, but the advantages they confer on an organism are not always clear. Toxins will be discussed in greater detail in Chapter 2.

Intestinal parasites in particular need protection from the digestive processes going on around them. This protection may consist of a cuticle for parasitic worms, or the ability of *Vibrio cholerae* to penetrate the protective mucus lining of the gut. Other protective adaptations include bacterial and protoctist **flagella**, which confer motility, and bacterial **capsules**, which confer resistance to phagocytosis. Finally, the organisms must get their progeny to a new host, since all hosts eventually die. Transmitting offspring to another host can be difficult, and parasites produce a large number of progeny, increasing the chances of at least some of them infecting new hosts. A single virus that infects a cell can give rise to many new virus particles, and one bacterium can quickly produce a large number of cells by repeated binary fission. The eukaryotic parasites also have phenomenal fecundity: the pork tapeworm, *Taenia solium*, for example, produces as many as a quarter of a million eggs *per day*. Other parasites increase the numbers of progeny they produce by reproducing several times during a single life cycle; for example, the malarial parasite reproduces four times in the course of one life cycle. Some parasites have highly resistant progeny that can persist for long periods in the external environment, such as protoctist cysts, and the spores of fungi and bacteria.

The difficulties encountered in transmitting progeny to a new host also compound the problems faced by parasites that reproduce sexually.

- ◯ What is the major problem faced by sexually reproducing organisms?

- ⬤ Finding a mate. The problem is particularly acute for organisms such as helminths, which are unlikely to find a member of the opposite sex conveniently in the same host.

This may be why some parasites are able to reproduce asexually or by **hermaphroditism**, involving the possession by one individual of both male and female sex organs. You will learn later (Chapters 6 and 7) about the complex life cycles of many eukaryotic parasites that have adapted to the problems posed by their lifestyle by using vectors and intermediate hosts.

1.3 The body's response to parasites

When parasites invade a human body, they are entering hostile territory where they may be recognized as non-self material and eliminated from the body's tissues. You may be surprised to learn that it is frequently our body's response to parasites, rather than features of the parasites themselves, that make us feel ill. There are a number of mechanisms that can counteract invaders, and these act at different levels. Some are automatic responses: coughing expels foreign particles from the respiratory tract, and vomiting expels many irritating substances from the gastrointestinal tract. We also have learned behaviours that tend to eliminate parasites: we wash our hands after touching infective material (even though such contact does not usually make us feel ill!). Probably the most sophisticated type of response is provided by the immune system, which continually monitors the body and tries to expel any invading organisms. These invaders are recognized as potentially harmful by their unique surface antigens. You have already come across surface antigens in the Influenza Case Study, and you might like to look back at it now to refresh your memory.

Many antigens are found on the surfaces of parasites, while others are found inside them and are released only when the parasites are degraded by the host, thereby becoming 'visible' to the immune system. Most antigens are large, complex protein molecules with a relative molecular mass greater than 5000; however, other large complex molecules such as polysaccharides and glycolipids may also serve as antigens. Large antigenic molecules like these are found on the cell surfaces of bacteria, fungi and protoctists. Viral antigens are usually components of the outer protein coat (the capsid) or the lipid envelope. Prions, which are protein molecules, do not seem to be antigenic at all, even though they are certainly large enough to be antigens. It is thought that these proteins resemble a host protein so very closely that the immune system is unable to recognize them.

It is often very difficult to determine exactly how the symptoms of a particular disease arise. Sometimes, the picture can be very clear, for example when the disease symptoms are caused entirely by a bacterial toxin, as in the respiratory infection diphtheria. However, in this disease, as in others, there is also an immune response, and this may itself make some contribution towards the symptoms. In fact, many of the symptoms we associate with 'being ill', such as fever, aches and pains, can be caused by our immune system's response to an infection, rather than the infectious agent itself. In the case of many viral infections, the symptoms are almost all the result of the host's immune response. Establishing the contribution of various components to disease symptoms is difficult, since even if a substance has a clear-cut activity *in vitro*, it may be hard to demonstrate the same activity *in vivo*.

Thus in many infections the symptoms experienced will result from the interaction of the infectious agent with the host and the immune response to that agent. **Fever** (higher than normal body temperature) is a good example of such a symptom, because even though infectious agents may produce **pyrogens** (fever-inducing substances), they alone are often insufficient to account for the rise in temperature observed. Fever is a common response to infection and was long thought to act against the infecting agent and aid recovery. As recently as the 1930s, syphilis patients were deliberately infected with malaria so that the resulting fever episodes would kill the bacterium causing the syphilis! The malaria was then cured with quinine. This drastic action did actually work, because the bacterium that causes syphilis, *Treponema pallidum*, is heat-sensitive and cannot survive repeated fevers. In the pre-antibiotic era, such bizarre treatments made sense. However, apart from its effect on *T. pallidum* (and, incidentally, the bacterium that causes gonorrhoea, which is also heat-sensitive), fever does not appear to have a clear role in killing infectious agents. The benefits of fever to the host may be more indirect; for example, it might aid the immune response against infectious agents. Fever will be examined again later, in Book 3.

1.4 Where do pathogens come from?

The evolutionary origin of pathogens is a far-reaching and interesting topic, which will be addressed in Book 5. Here we consider how hosts encounter pathogens.

Parasitism is only one way in which different species may live in close relationships with one another. A relationship of a different character is **commensalism** (literally 'eating at the same table') where one species, the **commensal**, benefits from food and possibly shelter while the host remains unaffected. Humans support vast numbers of commensal organisms, mostly bacteria, on their skin and on the mucous membranes of the respiratory, gastrointestinal and genitourinary tracts (for details, see Reference CD: S204 Book 4, Chapter 4). In a healthy body, these commensals do us no harm, and may even protect us from pathogens. If we benefit from the presence of our commensal flora, then the relationship we have with them is referred to as **mutualism**, since both the host and the organisms it supports benefit. However, the harmless inhabitants of our bodies are conventionally referred to as commensals.

Sometimes the balance between a host and a commensal shifts so that the commensal becomes a pathogen. This can happen when the host defences are damaged in some way; for example, cancer chemotherapy may damage the gut wall, allowing gut commensals into the bloodstream. This can result in life-threatening **septicaemia**, caused by the circulation and multiplication of bacteria in the blood. Commensals may also become pathogens when organisms from one part of the body are deposited in a region they don't normally inhabit. Faecal bacteria may contaminate the female urethra during defecation, leading to cystitis. The infections caused in this way are termed **endogenous**, because the causative agent originated from the host's own body.

○ Recall the name given to commensals that become pathogens.

● They are known as opportunistic pathogens.

An infection caused by an agent originating from *outside* the body is described as **exogenous** and has a more complicated history, since the infectious agent must first break through the body's defences. How exogenous agents achieve entry into their hosts and meet the demands made of a successful parasite is described below.

1.5 Routes of transmission

Before we go on to look at the various routes of transmission in detail, we need to consider the relationships of the hosts involved. The major routes of person-to-person transmission of infectious agents are airborne, arthropod-borne, direct contact and via the gastrointestinal tract. Normal person-to-person spread of an agent by any of these routes is described as **horizontal transmission**. There is another way that agents can be spread from person to person, known as **vertical transmission**. This describes the way that one generation, the parent, infects the next generation, the child, via sperm, ova (eggs), while a child is in the uterus, or during breast-feeding. Of course, parents can also infect their children by horizontal contact.

A fetus is protected from many infectious agents by the arrangement of the fetal and maternal blood supplies within the placenta. These blood supplies are not in direct contact, but separated by a layer a few cells thick. For an agent to cause *in utero* infection, it must overcome this barrier. The fetus does not make antibodies of its own, but is further protected by one type of maternal antibody, which can cross the barrier in the placenta. Despite this protection, a number of agents can still infect the fetus, such as the rubella virus and the protoctist *Toxoplasma gondii*, which causes toxoplasmosis. In adults, toxoplasmosis is usually a mild flu-like illness, but in fetuses it can cause congenital abnormalities, and even stillbirth.

1.5.1 Infection via the air

The air we breathe contains many suspended particles, and although most of these particles are composed of dust, soot and smoke, some of them are microbes. It has been estimated that we breathe in some 10 000 microbes per day, mainly non-pathogenic bacteria and fungi. However, sometimes these microbes are pathogenic, and the respiratory infections they cause are one of the most common types of infection the world over. The respiratory tract has very efficient mechanisms for coping with solid matter contained in the air. The nasal cavity is lined with a layer of mucus and ciliated epithelial cells. The mucus traps the particles and the cilia beat the mucus to the back of the throat where it is swallowed. A similar mechanism operates in the lower respiratory tract (i.e. the structures below the voice box) and is called the **mucociliary escalator**. The mucus layer stops at the alveoli (the blind ends of the bronchioles), which allows gaseous exchange to occur. (For details see Reference CD: SK220 Book 3, Chapter 2.) However, the alveoli are lined with macrophages, which phagocytose the particles that were missed by the mucociliary escalator. These mechanisms are normally so successful that the lower respiratory tract is kept aseptic (free of agents of disease).

○ Does 'aseptic' mean the same as 'sterile'?

▣ No. Sterile means the complete absence of living material, whereas aseptic, as indicated above, means the absence of undesirable living material. This distinction is important, as you will see later on.

In order to cause a respiratory tract infection, an organism must first gain entry to the respiratory tract and avoid being swept away by the mucociliary escalator. If it reaches the alveoli, it must avoid being killed by phagocytosis in the macrophages. If, on the other hand, it infects the upper respiratory tract, it will have to compete with the commensal flora. Respiratory pathogens have specific features that allow their adherence, persistence and growth in the respiratory tract. Other opportunistic pathogens can infect the respiratory tract if its defence mechanisms are damaged, such as by an existing infection. This is how a simple viral infection like a cold can lead to a more serious secondary bacterial infection, such as a chest infection.

Once an infection is established in the respiratory tract, transmission may occur by coughing, sneezing or simply talking. These activities release infective droplets. Larger droplets (of the order 10 μm diameter) fall to the ground within around a metre of where they left the host, but smaller droplets (1–4 μm diameter) can remain airborne for long periods and may be inhaled by those nearby. If the infectious agent can persist in these conditions, the air can remain contaminated for hours or even days. The viruses that cause colds and flu cannot survive for long in the air as they become dried out, and they require close proximity for infection of new hosts, but others, such as the foot-and-mouth disease virus from livestock, can travel for long distances carried on the wind. During the 2001 foot-and-mouth disease outbreak in the UK, wind-borne spread of the virus is thought to have been responsible for infecting sheep and cattle in the early stages of the epidemic. These animals lived a few miles from the farm in Northumberland that was identified as having the earliest case of foot-and-mouth disease.

If the damage caused by a microbe leads to an increase in mucus secretions entering the throat, the cough reflex is stimulated. Coughing projects organisms from the lungs, throat and mouth into the air, producing a few hundred infective droplets per cough. Many coughs are caused by viruses, and the viruses are spread by the coughing reflex they induce. Nasal discharge is another mechanism used by microbes for transmission. An increase in nasal discharge can cause sneezing, which produces up to 20 000 high-velocity droplets of varying size (see Figure 1.1).

The discharge inevitably ends up on the hands of the infected person too, so that colds may be spread by direct contact as well (see below). Airborne pathogens may also bind to dust particles, and those that persist in this state can cause serious problems in hospitals when the dust is disturbed and the organisms inhaled.

1.5.2 Transmission by contact

Infections can be transferred by direct person-to-person contact, or indirectly via another animal called a vector or an intermediate host, as well as by inanimate objects known as fomites. You are familiar from the Malaria Case Study with the idea of a vector, and with fomites from Book 1, Chapter 4, on hospital acquired infections. Fomites can be something as simple as a cup, plate or door-handle on which an infected person has left infectious microbes. A new host can become infected when they use the contaminated article.

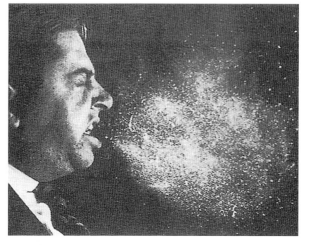

FIGURE 1.1
Droplets produced by a sneeze. Each droplet can contain thousands of microbes.

Intact human skin is a very effective barrier against invading microbes, so, although our skin represents the largest target for microbial attack, few pathogens can infect it or gain entry via this route. One exception is the bacterium *Leptospira interrogans*, frequently found in freshwater, which is able to penetrate intact skin and cause leptospirosis. This infection has a variety of symptoms ranging from a mild flu-like illness to a severe form of jaundice called Weil's disease. Some helminths are also able to gain entry directly through the skin surface (Chapter 7). The surface of the skin comprises a hard, horny layer of dead cells, and is very dry. The skin has a weakly acidic pH of around 5.5, and the high sodium chloride concentration found in sweat makes our body surfaces an osmotically stressful environment for microbes. Additionally, various antimicrobial substances are found on the skin surface, some of them produced by the resident flora. Gram-positive bacteria partially degrade complex lipids to fatty acids that are active against Gram-negative bacteria. Some of these fatty acids have a powerful, unpleasant odour, and for this reason deodorants target Gram-positive bacteria. However, with these bacteria out of the way, the skin may be left open to attack by Gram-negative bacteria instead. (We discuss Gram-positive and Gram-negative bacteria further in Chapter 2. You will find more information about them on the Reference CD: S204 Book 4, Chapter 1.)

None of these skin defences is effective against biting insects such as fleas, ticks, lice, mites and sand flies. These animals penetrate the skin with their feeding apparatus, reaching into the dermal (skin) tissues or even directly into the blood vessels. When these insects are themselves infected with pathogenic microbes, they are in effect injecting these microbes straight into our tissues. The organisms may be present in their saliva (for example, the yellow fever virus is transmitted in the saliva of the *Aedes aegyptii* mosquito), or in the gut contents regurgitated during a feed (the Black Death was transmitted in this way by fleas infected with the plague bacterium *Yersinia pestis*). Another source of infection is the faeces of the insect: Chagas' disease is caused by the entry of the reduviid bug's faeces, infected with the protoctist *Trypanosoma cruzi,* into a fresh bite-wound (see Section 5.3).

○ Recall the way in which the malaria parasite is transmitted.

● *Plasmodium* is present in the saliva of the infected female *Anopheles* mosquito.

Once skin is damaged, whether microscopically or macroscopically, the way is open for many pathogens to gain access. In these cases, the microbes are introduced directly onto or into the skin by human-to-human contact, or by objects passed between people (fomites). Rough contact sports such as rugby can be the source of staphylococcal skin infections, and hepatitis viruses can be contracted from contaminated needles. Bacteria from an animal's mouth may also be introduced into a wound during an animal attack, with the result that the wound turns septic. Worse still, if the animal is rabid, the bite victim may become infected with the rabies virus.

Other exterior surfaces of the body that can be infected by direct contact are the conjunctiva of the eyes, and the genitourinary tract. The conjunctiva is a thin, moist layer of living cells and therefore might seem an easier target than the skin. However, tears secreted from the lachrymal glands continually wash the eyes and this, together with the blinking action of the eyelids, sweeps any foreign particles away. The tears from the eyes then drain into the nose. The tears are not just a mechanical defence, as they contain antimicrobial substances such as the enzyme lysozyme, which degrades peptidoglycan, an important structural component of most bacterial cell walls (see Chapter 2). Only microbes with special abilities are able to attach and persist in this environment. One such microbe is the bacterium *Chlamydia trachomatis*, which is responsible for the eye disease known as trachoma. As with the skin, infection of the eye is made much easier if the outer surface is damaged. Conjunctivitis infections can start this way, following damage to the eye by rubbing with fingers, wearing contact lenses for too long, or prolonged exposure to chlorine in swimming pool water.

Perhaps the most obvious infections that can be transmitted by direct contact are the sexually transmissible ones. The warm, moist mucous membranes of living cells of the genitourinary tract offer an attractive habitat for microbes, and intimate contact allows the transfer of organisms that are unable to persist outside the body, such as the bacterium *Neisseria gonorrhoeae*, which causes gonorrhoea. However, the genitourinary tract is not unprotected. The regular flushing action of urine prevents colonization of the urethra, except by specialist pathogens such as some types of *E. coli* and *N. gonorrhoeae,* which cling on using pili. The *E. coli* bacterium is a major cause of urinary tract infections. The urethra is further protected by secreted antibodies, and in men the secretions from the prostate gland are antibacterial. From puberty to the menopause, the vagina is protected from harmful microbes by its acidic pH of 5.0. This low pH is produced by the action of a resident bacterium in the vagina known as Doderlein's bacillus. This bacterium metabolizes glycogen, present in the vaginal epithelium, to produce lactic acid, which reduces the pH. The uterus is protected by cilia and a downward flow of mucus at the cervix. Again, only specially adapted pathogens can establish an infection in this location.

1.5.3 Infection via food and water

The gastrointestinal tract is a major point of entry to, and exit from, the body. Every day this part of our bodies receives food and drink and various bodily secretions such as saliva. All the material expelled from the lungs by the mucociliary escalator, and carried by cilia and tears from the nose and eyes, is brought to the throat to be swallowed. During swallowing, the tongue is forced against the back of the throat and this provides some pathogens with a chance to establish an infection. You know from your own experience that many upper respiratory tract infections begin with a sore or tickly throat.

Much of our food contains microbes; some microbes, such as the bacteria found in live yogurt, we even eat deliberately, but few ever do us any harm. Helminths almost always enter orally, often as cyst stages in undercooked food, and the cysts rupture in the gut to release the parasites. Our defence against pathogenic microbes begins in the mouth, where microbes are continually washed away by saliva. The saliva also contains chemical weapons such as lysozyme and antibodies. If we breathe through our mouths, the throat acts as a baffle, restricting the flow of air so that suspended solid particles settle out and are deposited on it. This is similar to the action of the bones in the nose, which are covered by the nasal mucosa (surface layer) and act as baffles to air breathed in through the nose.

Most of the organisms that we swallow are killed in the 'acid bath' of our stomachs. This is made up of mucus, a layer of which prevents the stomach from digesting itself, a solution of hydrochloric acid with a pH of 3–4, and proteolytic (protein-digesting) enzymes. Of course, some microbes are adapted to survive in this hostile environment, and others can survive if they remain sheltered inside food particles. Many protoctist cysts (Chapter 5), picornaviruses (Chapter 3), helminths (Chapter 7) and some bacteria can survive in the stomach.

○ What would you predict to be the fate of microbial toxins in the stomach?

● Many toxins are proteins, so are likely to be denatured and thereby inactivated by the acid conditions and/or digested by the proteolytic enzymes present.

Stomach acid does indeed inactivate many microbial toxins, but those of *Clostridium* and *Staphylococcus* bacteria are able to persist and cause food poisoning. Survival is made easier for these pathogens if the pH of the stomach is raised, making it less acidic. Experiments with human volunteers showed that increasing the stomach pH by ingestion of 2 g of sodium bicarbonate led to a dramatic fall in the number of organisms required to initiate infections with *Salmonella* bacteria (food poisoning) and *Vibrio cholerae* bacteria (cholera). One bacterium, *Helicobacter pylori*, is actually adapted to live in the gastric environment and may persist there for many years. We will be returning to this curious microbe later, in the chapter on diseases with an unexpected infectious aetiology (Chapter 8).

There is one final action the stomach can take when harmful substances are detected inside it, and that is to expel the contents through the mouth as vomit. The **vomiting reflex** is a means to remove harmful substances quickly from the gut and relies on the coordinated activity of a number of muscles. Harmful substances in the gut are detected by chemoreceptors that relay information to the so-called vomiting centre in the brainstem. These stimuli then activate the vomiting centre, and the stomach contents are rapidly expelled.

The microbes and helminths that survive to reach the small intestine must now resist the action of digestive enzymes and bile, which would break them down to their constituent components, just as these digestive secretions break down our food. Would-be pathogens also need to attach themselves to the gut wall, to avoid being swept away in the continuous downward movement of the gut contents. Attachment is made more difficult by the daily shedding of the epithelial cells that line the gastrointestinal tract, and by the presence of a thick layer of protective mucus containing antibodies. Some pathogenic bacteria, such as *Vibrio cholerae* and some *E. coli*, are motile and can seek out attachment sites. Viruses, on the other hand, have no means of propulsion and rely on the peristaltic mixing and churning movements of the gut to bring them into contact with the intestinal epithelial cells. Helminths gain attachment by specialized hooks or suckers, or sometimes both.

The microbes that penetrate the gastrointestinal tract are not entering virgin territory. As the distance from the stomach increases, so does the density of the commensal gut flora. Around 10^{14} bacteria are believed to inhabit the human body, and most of them are found in the gut. These organisms play an important protective role, since pathogens must compete with them for nutrients and attachment sites. The commensal flora also produce some inhibitory substances that help them to hold their own in this fiercely competitive world, and these inhibitors may be detrimental to pathogens. The importance of the protection conferred by these commensals is demonstrated when their numbers become unevenly reduced as a result of antibiotic therapy. The antibiotics kill some of the commensal flora along with the pathogens they are intended to eliminate. This depletion of commensal microbes can lead to diarrhoea and the overgrowth of selected organisms, such as the yeast *Candida albicans* in the mouth, which causes thrush. Overgrowth of the bacterium *Clostridium difficile* in the intestine can cause diarrhoea, or a serious infection known as pseudomembranous colitis.

In fact, many gastrointestinal infections result in diarrhoea, and it is unclear whether this is a host defence to eliminate pathogens or a microbial adaptation that allows transmission to other hosts. **Diarrhoea**, the passing of liquid faeces or faeces that lack shape, certainly expels pathogens from the gastrointestinal tract as quickly as possible. The increase in the flow rate of the gut contents also allows less time for microbial growth. However, diarrhoea is also an excellent vehicle for transmission, especially where faecal material ends up in food or water. When pathogens are transmitted via faecally contaminated food or water, the transmission route is described as the **faecal–oral route**.

This chapter has introduced you to the extraordinarily diverse group of organisms that cause disease in humans. In it you have seen how pathogens exploit our tissues as a food source, and the challenges they must meet in order to be successful. In the next six chapters, we will look at each group of pathogens in turn, and examine some of the effects that their presence may have on our bodies. Finally, in Chapter 8, we will consider other diseases that might have an infectious origin, and some diseases that have only recently been found to be caused by microbes.

Summary of Chapter 1

1   Biological agents of disease include representatives of helminths and protoctists (generally called parasites), fungi, bacteria and viruses (generally called pathogens) and prions (infectious proteins).

2   Koch's postulates are widely used to determine the identity of the causative agent of a disease.

3   Parasites, including pathogenic microbes, are specially adapted to penetrate a host, spread within it, and produce and release progeny, without succumbing to the host's defence systems.

4   The symptoms of disease are often caused by the body's response to the disease agent, as well as by the agent itself.

5   Infectious diseases can have endogenous or exogenous causes.

6   Routes of horizontal transmission of exogenous agents are via the air, via direct contact, or via food and water; vertical transmission occurs from mother to fetus or newborn.

Learning outcomes for Chapter 1

When you have studied this chapter, you should be able to:

1.1   Define and use, or recognize definitions and applications of, each of the terms printed in **bold** in the text. (*Questions 1.1, 1.2 and 1.3*)

1.2   Name the main groups of biological agents of disease. (*Question 1.1*)

1.3   Describe, using named examples, how agents of disease are adapted to their pathogenic lifestyle. (*Question 1.3*)

1.4   Explain how host responses to infection can cause symptoms of illness. (*Question 1.2*)

1.5   Explain the routes of infection used by endogenous and exogenous pathogens. (*Questions 1.2 and 1.3*)

Questions for Chapter 1

Question 1.1

Make a list of the main groups of pathogen, and for each give an example of a disease caused by this type of agent, that you have met so far in the course.

Question 1.2

List the main points of entry to the body of infectious agents and the first-line host defences for each infection route.

Question 1.3

Compare the adaptations shown by some bacteria and some helminths to a lifestyle inside a host's gut.

2 THE BACTERIA

There are three case studies associated with this chapter, to which you are directed at the appropriate points in the text.

CASE STUDY

We begin this chapter with a note on nomenclature. As in other kingdoms of the living world, each species of bacteria has a generic and a specific name, both of which are written in italics. However, many microbiologists and medical personnel use a 'short-hand' nomenclature when it is not necessary to identify individual species. Thus, if the subject is an unknown member of the genus *Salmonella*, the bacteria may simply be called 'salmonellae' (no italics). Likewise, when considering faecal contamination of water, it is unnecessary to distinguish species, and the contaminants may be referred to as 'coliforms', i.e. bacteria like (or even unlike!) *E. coli*. In the following text, as in others, you will come across both types of nomenclature. More information about this topic is given in Box 2.1.

BOX 2.1 Bacterial nomenclature

As you study S320 you may find it hard to manage the many names of bacteria that you encounter, and you might be confused by the different ways that these names can be written. This box is designed to clear up any difficulties, so that you can concentrate fully on the course content.

The kingdom Bacteria is classified into orders, families, genera and species in much the same way as the plant and animal kingdoms, which may be more familiar to you (although see below). Each bacterium has a Latin name, which is italicized, consisting of a genus name with a capital first letter followed by a species name, e.g. *Escherichia coli*. Once the full name has been given, the genus name may be abbreviated to the first letter when the bacterium is mentioned again, e.g. *E. coli*. However, if species from several genera are under discussion and the genera names all begin with the same letter, then each genus name may be abbreviated to the first few letters instead, to make clear which genus a bacterium belongs to. For instance, you may already know the alternative abbreviation '*Staph.*' used for *Staphylococcus*, as in *Staph. aureus*, and '*Strep.*' for *Streptococcus*, as in *Strep. faecalis*.

If all the species from a particular genus are being discussed, then the genus name can be given a plural ending and be written non-italicized and without a capital letter. For example, if we are discussing the bacteria in the genus *Mycobacterium*, e.g. *Mycobacterium tuberculosis* and *Mycobacterium leprae* (the causative agents of tuberculosis and leprosy respectively), then we might refer to them collectively as mycobacteria. Knowing which ending to add to which genus names is made easier by following a few rules:

If the genus name ends in:		Changing it to the plural gives:	
-ium	e.g. *Mycobacterium*	-ia	e.g. mycobacteria
-a	e.g. *Chlamydia*	-ae	e.g. chlamydiae
-coccus	e.g. *Staphylococcus*	-cocci	e.g. staphylococci

There are some exceptions to these rules. The genus *Treponema*, which includes *T. pallidum* (the species that causes syphilis), is referred to in the plural as 'treponemes' and *not* the expected 'treponemae'. There is another potential source of confusion: what would be the plural form of the genus *Bacillus*? The answer is 'bacilli', but this term is also used to refer to any rod-shaped bacteria, so must be interpreted with care.

(Box 2.1 continues overleaf.)

Sometimes species within a genus are referred to without giving the species name: if one species within a genus is referred to in this way the abbreviation 'sp.' is used after the genus name, e.g. *Mycobacterium* sp.; and if several species are being referred to, then 'spp.' is used, e.g. *Mycobacterium* spp. As you can see, the abbreviations for 'species' are not italicized.

Other conventions that you may come across in your further reading concern the names of bacterial families and orders, which are also given in Latin. Family names always end in -aceae, e.g. Enterobacteriaceae (the family to which *E. coli* belongs) and order names always end in -ales, e.g. Vibrionales (the order that includes *Vibrio cholerae*, the causative agent of cholera).

Medical nomenclature

Since this course is about infectious disease, we have had to use some medical terms to describe the signs and symptoms of the various diseases. These are easier to understand if you know the meaning of certain word-endings (suffixes):

Suffix	Meaning of suffix
-itis	inflamed, e.g. cystitis means inflammation of the bladder
-aemia	in the blood, e.g. viraemia means viruses in the blood; bacteraemia means the transient presence of bacteria in the blood and septicaemia is a clinically significant, life-threatening response to the presence and multiplication of bacteria in the blood
-tomy	cutting of, e.g. tracheotomy means cutting the windpipe or trachea

An important reminder

Although for biological convenience we refer to 'species' of bacteria, this term is fairly meaningless. In the wider biological world, species are often defined as populations of potentially interbreeding individuals. This always presents problems for non-sexually reproducing organisms, and this group includes bacteria, which increase in numbers by binary fission. However, bacteria are adept at shuffling around DNA by various mechanisms, some of which involve individuals of different 'species'. This makes a nonsense of taxonomic classification based on similarity of DNA sequences.

◯ Why is it difficult to establish taxonomic relationships between bacteria?

⬤ A random event such as transformation with a DNA molecule from the wider environment could make a bacterium appear taxonomically closer to another species than is actually the case, because they appear to share significant amounts of DNA sequence.

Further, because bacteria are haploid (they have only one set of chromosomes per cell), mutations are immediately expressed in the phenotype. Depending on the mutation rate, a 'pure' culture of a particular species of bacterium might actually contain hundreds (or thousands) of individuals with genomes that differ from the 'standard' for that species. Thus a pathogenic individual might arise *de novo* in a previously harmless species. Is it still a member of that species? To avoid this difficult question, microbiologists have adopted a different kind of nomenclature. Rather than invoking new species each time a phenotypically different organism appears, they refer to different **strains** of a species. Thus, although the vast majority of *E. coli* are non-pathogenic, there are a few pathogenic strains – still *E. coli*, but different from the 'conventional' sort.

2.1 The range and diversity of bacteria

Bacteria are single-celled organisms and are probably the oldest forms of life on the planet. Fossilized bacteria have been found that date back to around 3.5 billion years ago (see Figure 2.1). Bacteria are the most widely distributed living organisms on Earth. They are the predominant microbes in the soil, and can also be found in the most inhospitable environments, such as around hydrothermal vents deep under water where temperatures may reach 113 °C, or in the freezing conditions of the Poles. Bacteria also exploit the environments available to them in, or on, plants and animals. Healthy animals have characteristic microbial populations, made up largely of bacteria, their commensal flora. In plants such as peas and clover, bacteria are found in root nodules where they fix nitrogen and make it available to their hosts. Nitrogen fixation is the process by which nitrogen gas (N_2) in the atmosphere is chemically reduced to ammonia (NH_3). This is a crucial process, since nitrogen is a major component of living things, but only nitrogen-fixing organisms can use the rich source in the atmosphere – almost 80% of the air is nitrogen gas. Most living things depend on nitrogen-containing compounds for their nitrogen requirements, and nearly all of these compounds originate from the process of nitrogen fixation. Bacteria alone are able to fix atmospheric nitrogen, and they also play an important role in the geochemical cycling of other elements such as carbon, sulfur and iron. In terms of their nutrition, bacteria are broadly divided into autotrophs (obtaining their energy from sunlight) and heterotrophs (obtaining their energy from chemical compounds), and they can exploit an enormous variety of substrates.

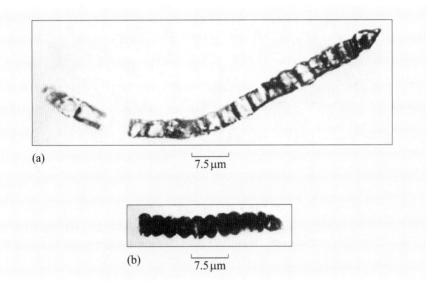

(a) 7.5 μm

(b) 7.5 μm

FIGURE 2.1
Fossilized microbes from the Bitter Springs formation in Central Australia.

By virtue of their metabolic versatility, bacteria are widely used in industries as diverse as mining, sewage treatment, pharmaceuticals and foods, where reactions carried out by bacteria can perform steps that are impossible, or unfeasible, by other means. In recent years, the advances of molecular biology have led to ever more sophisticated methods of exploiting bacteria, and their components, in the industry known as **biotechnology**. Unfortunately, some bacteria also have very unwelcome effects: they cause spoilage of foods and are major pathogens of both humans and animals. It is this last group that we consider here, and we begin with an overview of bacterial structure.

2.2 The bacterial cell wall

Bacteria are prokaryotes, which means their cells lack the membrane-bound organelles found in the more complicated eukaryotic cells.

◯ From your previous reading, name these organelles.

⬤ The most obvious is the nucleus. Others are mitochondria, chloroplasts, endoplasmic reticulum and Golgi, and endosomes of various sorts.

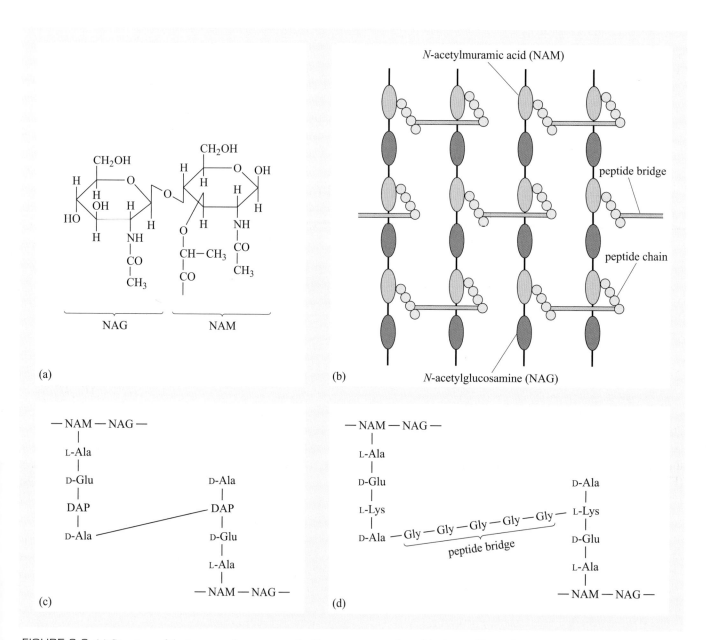

FIGURE 2.2 (a) Structure of the two complex monosaccharide components of peptidoglycan, *N*-acetylmuramic acid (NAM) and *N*-acetylglucosamine (NAG). You need not remember the details of these structures. (b) A section of peptidoglycan showing how adjacent chains are cross-linked. (c) Direct cross-linking between NAM tetrapeptides. (d) Indirect cross-linking via a peptide bridge comprising five glycine residues (pentaglycine).

The Bacteria, along with the Archaea, make up the prokaryotes; all other organisms have eukaryotic cells, with a distinct nucleus and organelles, and are called eukaryotes. Apart from some wall-less forms of Bacteria, all prokaryotes have a cell wall, which protects them from osmotic and mechanical damage. Some also have one or more extra coatings in the form of polysaccharide or protein layers, variously called capsules, slime layers or glycocalyx (see below). The cell wall often confers a characteristic shape on an organism: for example rod-shaped (bacillus, plural: bacilli) or ball-shaped (coccus, plural: cocci). In Bacteria (but not Archaea) the cell wall nearly always contains **peptidoglycan**, (also known as murein), which is a high-molecular-mass polymer (i.e. it's big!) found nowhere else. The details of peptidoglycan structure vary from species to species, but the basic framework remains the same, and is shown in Figure 2.2.

Peptidoglycan is made up of two complex monosaccharides, *N*-acetylmuramic acid (NAM) and *N*-acetylglucosamine (NAG) (Figure 2.2a), which alternate to form a polysaccharide chain. Several polysaccharide chains lie parallel to one another and are held together by cross-links between them (Figure 2.2b). The cross-links form between tetrapeptides (lengths of four amino acids) attached to each NAM, and when two NAM molecules lie close together, their tetrapeptides become cross-linked, either directly, as in *E. coli* (Figure 2.2c), or indirectly, by the involvement of further amino acids such as the pentaglycine bridge found in *Staphylococcus aureus* peptidoglycan (Figure 2.2d). This cross-linking between adjacent NAG–NAM polysaccharide chains gives the peptidoglycan structure great strength. Among the amino acids making up the tetrapeptides of NAM are three that are unique to bacteria: D-glutamic acid (D-Glu), D-alanine (D-Ala) and *meso*-diamino-pimelic acid (DAP).

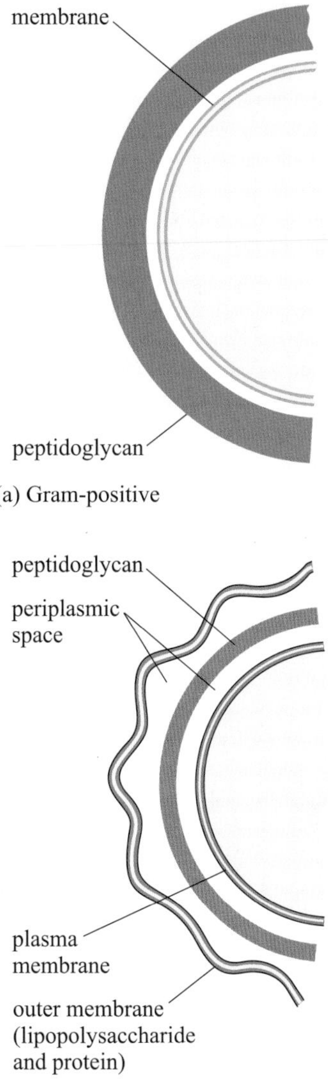

○ What is unusual about the first two of these amino acids?

● They are in the D form; elsewhere in the living world, amino acids occur only in the L form. (Don't worry if you aren't familiar with L and D forms – just note the rarity of D amino acids.)

Bacteria are divided into two major groups called Gram-positive and Gram-negative, depending on their reaction to a staining procedure known as the Gram stain. The Gram stain differentiates bacteria with respect to the structure of their cell walls. Gram-positive bacteria have a cytoplasmic or plasma membrane bounded by a thick layer of peptidoglycan, while Gram-negative bacteria have a plasma membrane, a thin layer of peptidoglycan and then an additional second or **outer membrane**. (Figure 2.3).

The Gram-positive cell wall has up to 40 layers of peptidoglycan and is between 20 and 80 nm thick (see Figure 2.4 overleaf). The peptidoglycan may comprise up to 90% of the dry mass of the bacterium. The peptidoglycan layers are cross-linked to each other, forming one enormous cell-shaped peptidoglycan molecule. Other cell wall constituents are teichoic (pronounced 'tie-ko-ic') and lipoteichoic (pronounced 'lie-po-tie-ko-ic') acids, which are polymers of glycerol or ribitol (a 5-carbon alcohol) that have short side-chains and are joined by phosphate groups (Figure 2.5 overleaf). The teichoic acids are covalently attached to the NAM component of the peptidoglycan, while lipoteichoic acids are fixed to lipids in the plasma membrane. These acids can make up half the cell wall structure. Their function is unclear, but the lipoteichoic acid appears to hold the peptidoglycan and plasma membrane

membrane

peptidoglycan

(a) Gram-positive

peptidoglycan

periplasmic space

plasma membrane

outer membrane (lipopolysaccharide and protein)

(b) Gram-negative

FIGURE 2.3
Arrangement of peptidoglycan in
(a) Gram-positive and
(b) Gram-negative bacteria.

together (Figure 2.4). Both polymers project from the peptidoglycan surface of Gram-positive bacteria, such as *Staphylococcus aureus*, and are their main surface antigens. Their negative charges also contribute to the overall negative charge of the bacterial cell.

FIGURE 2.4
Molecular arrangement of the Gram-positive cell surface. Only a few of the many peptidoglycan layers are shown.

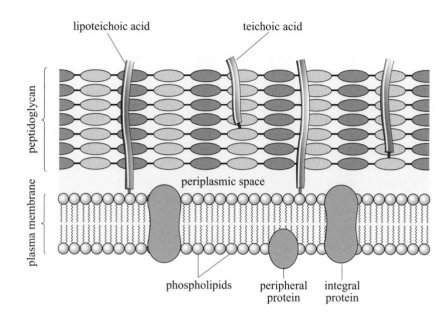

Gram-negative bacteria, such as *E. coli*, typically have only one or two layers of peptidoglycan 2–7 nm across (Figure 2.6). To the exterior of this thin peptidoglycan layer lies the outer membrane, and on either side of the peptidoglycan is a region called the **periplasmic space**. The periplasmic space acts as a buffer between the cell contents and the external environment, and is not a 'space' at all, although it looks 'empty' when examined by microscopy. This region is actually so full of enzymes, metabolites and substances being transported into and out of the bacterium that it is highly viscous in nature.

The outer membrane of Gram-negative bacteria is not the same as the inner, cytoplasmic membrane. Firstly, it is more permeable than the inner membrane, since protein complexes called **porins** span the membrane and act as channels for a number of solutes. In addition, numerous lipoprotein (a lipid–protein complex) molecules link the peptidoglycan and the inner leaflet of the outer membrane. These lipoproteins, also known as Braun's lipoprotein, are the most abundant proteins found in Gram-negative bacteria. One end of the lipoprotein is covalently linked to the peptidoglycan and the other, hydrophobic, end is inserted into the outer membrane.

The outer leaflet (layer) of the outer membrane is also different from the corresponding region of the cytoplasmic membrane, since the phospholipid molecules are all replaced by **lipopolysaccharides** (LPS). LPS may comprise as much as 40% of the cell surface structure of a Gram-negative bacterium. LPS molecules are made up of a complex lipid called lipid A, joined to a negatively charged core polysaccharide which contributes to the overall negative charge of the bacterium, and a so-called O side-chain (Figure 2.7).

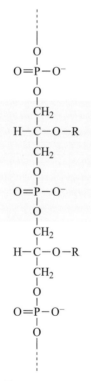

FIGURE 2.5
The structure of a teichoic acid, with one of the glycerol phosphate monomer units highlighted. Only a small part of the teichoic acid polymer is shown here; the whole molecule may be more than 30 units long. The R side-chain may be glucose, D-alanine, or other molecules. (You need not remember the details of this structure.)

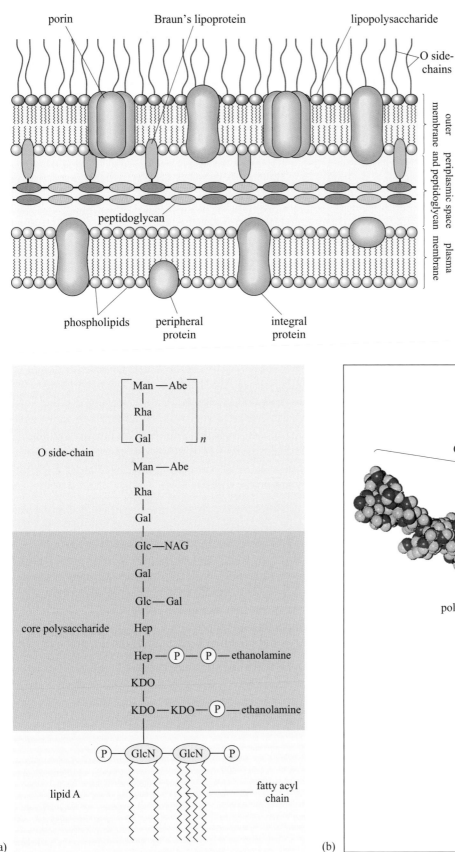

porin Braun's lipoprotein lipopolysaccharide

O side-chains

outer membrane

periplasmic space and peptidoglycan

plasma membrane

peptidoglycan

phospholipids peripheral protein integral protein

(a)

FIGURE 2.6
Molecular arrangement of the Gram-negative envelope.

FIGURE 2.7
Lipopolysaccharide structure. (a) Molecular organization of the *Salmonella* LPS. (Man = mannose, Abe = abequose, Rha = rhamnose, Gal = galactose, Hep = heptose, KDO = keto-deoxyoctanoate, Glc = glucose; GlcN = glucosamine; these molecules are are all monosaccharides or monosaccharide derivatives. 'n' = an integer.) (b) Space-filling model of the *E. coli* LPS. Notice that the O side-chain lies at an angle to the lipid A and core polysaccharide.

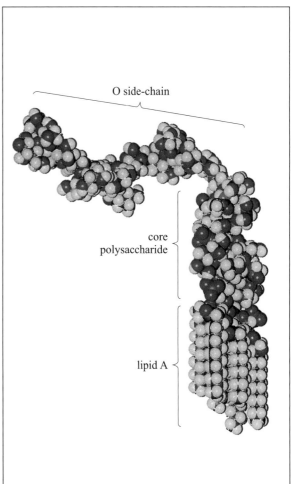

O side-chain

core polysaccharide

lipid A

(b)

The lipid A of *Salmonella typhimurium* has been studied extensively and it resembles membrane phospholipids, in that it has fatty acid tails that sit in the membrane and phosphate head groups. However, the phosphate groups are linked by two glucosamine units, which are attached to the core polysaccharide. This core polysaccharide, along with the O side-chain, projects from the bacterial cell surface. The O side-chain is a short polysaccharide that varies in composition between species, and between strains within a species. Since antibodies readily bind O side-chains, these chains are also called O antigens, and they are major targets for antibody and the complement system. The complement system is a complex defence mechanism, and you will learn about it in Book 3. One complement component acts by binding to the O antigen and causing lysis of the bacterium. If the O chains are long (i.e. *n* is large), the lytic activity of complement occurs too far away from the cell surface to lyse the bacterium, which thus remains undamaged. The extent to which O chains project from a bacterium is therefore a key factor in pathogenesis. O antigens can be useful for diagnosis too, since they allow different strains of the same species to be distinguished from one another (see Book 4).

Not all bacteria are easily Gram-stained; mycobacteria, for example, stain only very reluctantly and unpredictably. The name 'mycobacteria' means 'fungus bacteria' and refers to the structures resembling fungal hyphae (Section 6), which may develop when their cells form attachments with one another. Mycobacteria need to be heated with a dye for them to take it up, in a procedure known as the Ziehl–Neelsen stain (Figure 2.8). Once stained, the dye cannot be removed using acid, so these bacteria are described as **acid-fast**, although this is a functional rather than a biological classification. Mycobacteria have very waxy, lipid-rich cell walls, and this might explain how they can resist chemicals, macrophages and many antimicrobial agents. The corynebacteria, including *Corynebacterium diphtheriae*, the causative agent of diphtheria, have a similar cell wall structure to the mycobacteria, though unlike the mycobacteria, they are not acid-fast.

Acid-fast bacteria have only one membrane, so they are classified as Gram-positive. A peptidoglycan layer surrounds the plasma membrane, but the similarity to Gram-positives ends there (Figure 2.9). Covalently linked to the peptidoglycan are polymers of arabinose and galactose, which form a branched-chain arabinogalactan backbone. Some of the arabinose units are joined to a substance called **mycolic acid**. Mycolic acid is a complex, 60–90-carbon fatty acid, which is largely responsible for the waxy nature of mycobacterial cell walls.

The covalently bonded peptidoglycan–arabinogalactan–mycolic acid structure described above is also complexed non-covalently with other lipids, glycolipids and proteins. A major glycolipid is **lipo-arabinomannan** (LAM), and it plays an important role in the pathogenesis of *Mycobacterium tuberculosis*, which is the causative agent of tuberculosis. You will learn more about this microbe and the disease that it causes in the Tuberculosis Case Study (see below).

Another genus of bacteria that does not stain with the Gram stain is *Treponema*, which includes the causative agent of syphilis, *Treponema pallidum*. These bacteria, together with the genus *Borrelia*, which do take up the Gram stain, comprise the spirochaetes. Spirochaetes are long, slender rod-shaped bacteria, wound into spirals, and able to move through very viscous liquids and across solid surfaces (Figure 2.10). They are classified as Gram-negative bacteria since they have a cytoplasmic membrane bounded by a thin peptidoglycan layer, beyond which is an

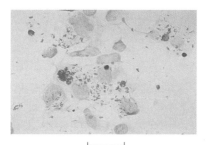

20 μm

FIGURE 2.8
Ziehl–Neelsen staining of a nasal sample from a patient with leprosy, showing the red-staining *Mycobacterium leprae*.

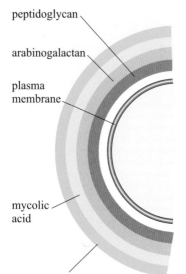

peptidoglycan

arabinogalactan

plasma membrane

mycolic acid

lipo-arabinomannan (LAM) and other glycolipids

FIGURE 2.9
Schematic representation of the cell wall of *Mycobacterium tuberculosis*.

outer membrane, known as a **sheath**. However, they differ from other Gram-negative bacteria in terms of their structure and motility. Their movement is dependent on flagella, but unlike most flagella, these lie just *beneath* the outer sheath and do not project from the cell surface. Despite their unusual location, the spirochaete flagella are composed of flagellin proteins that are genetically related to those found in the flagella of other bacteria. The flagella, also known as **axial fibrils** (see Figure 2.11), are anchored to the cell at either end and wrapped around the peptidoglycan layer, as can be seen in Figure 2.12. These flagella move the cell with its characteristic corkscrew motion, but the exact mechanism is not fully understood.

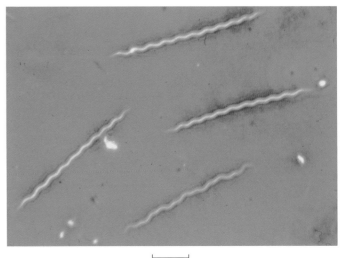

3 µm

FIGURE 2.10 *Treponema pallidum*, the spirochaete that causes syphilis.

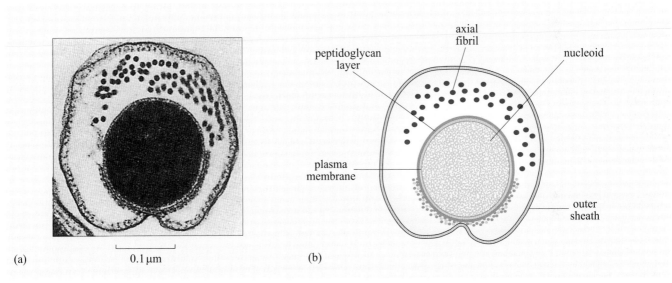

(a)   0.1 µm   (b)

FIGURE 2.11 (a) Electron micrograph of a cross-section of *Clevelandia*, a termite pathogen, showing the outer sheath and cross-sections of the axial fibrils. (b) Diagram of the electron micrograph shown in (a).

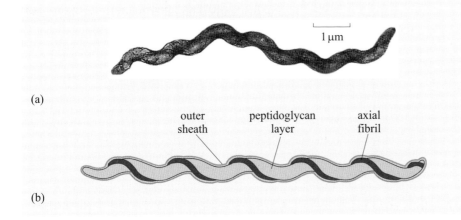

FIGURE 2.12
(a) Electron micrograph of *Treponema zuelzerae* with axial fibrils extending most of the bacterium's length. (b) Diagrammatic interpretation of the electron micrograph in (a).

The outer sheath of treponemes is unusually rich in lipids compared to the outer membranes of other Gram-negative bacteria, and that of *Treponema pallidum* also lacks some of the usual cell surface proteins. These differences in composition may account for the weakness of the host antibody response to this bacterium.

> **CASE STUDY**
>
> You will learn more about *Treponema pallidum* and the disease that it causes, in the Syphilis Case Study. This case study consists of a TV programme (which you should already have videotaped) and associated notes. Although it is suitable for study at any time, and you may wish to view the programme more than once, now would be a good time to view it, and to work through the notes, if you have not already done so.

2.2.1 Selective toxicity

In the previous section, you encountered substances that are unique to bacteria, such as the peptidoglycan found in most bacterial cell walls. Such substances can be targets for antibacterial **antibiotics.** Antibiotics are chemicals traditionally produced by microbes, that kill or inhibit the growth of other microbes, and they are used by humans to treat infectious disease. Some commonly used antibiotics are actually chemically modified versions of the microbial molecules, and still others, such as chloramphenicol, are made entirely by chemical synthesis. Antibiotics directed against targets like peptidoglycan can kill or harm bacteria without harming their human hosts, since humans lack these targets. Such antibiotics are said to demonstrate **selective toxicity**.

The best-known example of an antibiotic with selective toxicity is penicillin, which inhibits the synthesis of peptidoglycan. The original penicillin, obtained from the fungus *Penicillium chrysogenum*, was active only against Gram-positive bacteria (which have a lot of peptidoglycan), but more reactive penicillin derivatives can also act on Gram-negative bacteria. Penicillins are completely inactive against any species that does not make peptidoglycan, including, of course, humans. Some other antibacterial antibiotics in clinical use, and their targets, are shown in Table 2.1.

The principle of selective toxicity is used to combat infections caused by other infectious agents as well, such as viruses and fungi. In each case, targets are sought that are present in the infectious agent but absent from the host, or sufficiently different from those of the host to leave the host's tissues unharmed. These ideas were examined in S204 *Uniformity and Diversity*, Book 4, Chapter 7, Sections 7.2.3 and 7.3, and you can read this material from the Reference CD. If you are unfamiliar with the principle of selective toxicity, these sections will be a useful introduction for you. We will return to the concept of selective toxicity again in Book 7, where we look at strategies for combating infectious disease.

TABLE 2.1 Some antibiotics in clinical use and their targets.

Class or name	Example	Target	Comments
β-lactams	penicillin	peptidoglycan synthesis	active mainly against Gram-positives
glycopeptide	vancomycin	D-Ala–D-Ala bridges	active only against Gram-positives
isoniazid	isoniazid	mycolic acid synthesis	used against mycobacteria
tetracyclines	tetracycline	30S ribosome subunit	broad spectrum
macrolides	erythromycin	50S ribosome subunit	broad spectrum
aminoglycosides	gentamicin	30S ribosome subunit	active against aerobic bacteria, excluding streptococci
quinolones	nalidixic acid	bacterial DNA topoisomerases	active against Gram-negatives
rifamycins	rifampicin	initiation of RNA synthesis	active against *M. tuberculosis* and aerobic Gram-positive cocci
antimetabolites	trimethoprim	folic acid synthesis	broad spectrum, including some protoctists

2.3 Pathogenic bacteria

Of all the bacterial species in existence, relatively few are pathogenic for humans. The bacteria of the commensal flora actually protect the host by forcing the pathogens to compete for the available space and nutrients. Some commensals produce antimicrobial substances, which enable them to hold their own in the highly competitive environment of the gut, and these substances may also inhibit pathogens. Any disturbance to the intestinal commensal flora may predispose the host to disease, but **probiotics** may be able to restore or maintain the healthy balance of this community. Probiotics are substances, including living microbes, that promote the health or growth of a human. Probiotics are taken orally and often contain lactose-fermenting bacteria such as *Bifidobacterium* spp. and *Lactobacillus acidophilus*. Sources of probiotics include food and drink, e.g. Yakult, and dietary supplements, e.g. Multibionta probiotic multivitamins. However, their effectiveness is controversial: these species do not colonize the gut, so probiotics need to be taken every day. It is estimated that about three litres of *Lactobacillus* drink need to be ingested per day for the bacteria to be detected among the normal commensal species! There are probably easier ways of maintaining a healthy gut flora.

Defining a bacterium as a pathogen is not always straightforward. Some individuals carry recognized pathogenic bacteria as part of their commensal flora and never succumb to any disease they cause. Such individuals are termed **asymptomatic carriers** and may serve as a source of infection for others. An example of this is *Neisseria meningitidis*, which causes one type of meningitis, yet may be carried harmlessly in the nose. Commensal bacteria may become opportunistic pathogens if the host becomes compromised in some way.

○ What is the term used to describe an infection when the infecting organism originates *within* the host?

● Such infections are termed *endogenous* infections.

Not all infections result in disease: most are asymptomatic, with clinical disease developing only in the unfortunate few. This has been tragically demonstrated when patients have been inoculated with dangerous pathogens by mistake. A famous example of this was the so-called Lubeck disaster of 1926, when 249 babies were vaccinated with living *Mycobacterium tuberculosis*. Of the 249 exposed in this way 76 died of tuberculosis, but the remainder showed only minor symptoms. The outcome of each infection is therefore not entirely predictable, but is dependent on host factors. These factors include host genome, age, sex, nutritional status, pre-existing conditions, and so on. However, the nature of the pathogen is important too, as you will see next.

2.4 Virulence factors

In order to fully understand this section, you need to know some basic facts about plasmids, transposons and toxins. The essential background material is on the Reference CD (S204 Book 4, Chapters 4 and 5), and you are advised to revise it at this point, or study it if you have not passed S204. A brief aide-memoire about transposons and plasmids is given in Box 2.2.

BOX 2.2   Mobile genetic elements

There are several kinds of mobile genetic elements, that is, pieces of DNA that can move from one cell to another, and from one place to another within a single cell. Most bacteria have many and variable mobile elements in their genomes, and this is one reason why it is so difficult to define a bacterial 'species' on the basis of its DNA sequence.

Transposons are short sequences flanked by inverted repeats that allow the transposon to insert into, and come out from, a longer DNA sequence, by recombination. If a gene is present between the inverted repeats, then the gene is carried from place to place by the transposon's activity. Some transposons leave a copy of themselves where they have been; thus any gene in the transposon can spread through a population of cells.

Plasmids are small, self-replicating circles of DNA that vary in size but are generally large enough to carry a few genes. They may or may not be able to integrate stably into the bacterial chromosome, but many can initiate their own replication and transfer to neighbouring bacteria. Not all plasmids confer antibiotic resistance, but those that do typically carry one or two, and even up to five or six, antibiotic resistance genes. Recombination within a cell between different plasmids carrying different genes can result in the generation of entirely new plasmids carrying new combinations of, for example, antibiotic resistance genes.

Virulence is a measure of the ease with which an organism is able to cause damage and disease in host tissues: the more virulent the organism, the more easily host tissues are damaged. Any bacterial products that contribute to virulence are termed **virulence factors**.

○ At what levels might virulence factors act?

● Virulence factors might target the host, debilitating it or counteracting its defences, or they might act at the level of the bacterium, improving its effectiveness as a pathogen by, for example, increasing the secretion of a substance that inhibits competing microbes.

Virulence factors can be substances that aid bacterial nutrition (acting on the bacterium), facilitate spread (acting on the host), or mediate attachment (acting on both host and bacterium).

Genes for virulence factors are often found on transmissible plasmids or other mobile genetic elements such as transposons (see Box 2.2). These elements typically encode genes that allow the bacterium to survive in otherwise hostile environments, in this case human tissues. Plasmids may also encode genes that confer antibiotic resistance on bacteria carrying them. The most dangerous property of plasmids is the ease with which they may be transferred both within and between species. This transfer is an example of horizontal spread of a trait (in this case, one that is advantageous to the bacterium, rather than disease-causing), although vertical transmission to daughter bacteria does also occur. Plasmids can spread virulence factors through a whole population of bacterial cells in a very short time, and are an important evolutionary mechanism. Figure 2.13 shows an example of the rapid spread of plasmids within a bacterial population. The situation is made even more fluid when transposons are brought into the picture, as these 'jumping genes' can transfer material from plasmid to plasmid and from the bacterial chromosome to plasmids, or vice versa. Evidence suggests that these gene transfers within individual bacteria are responsible for the evolution of **pathogenicity islands**. These are particular regions in bacterial genomes that encode virulence factors. Pathogenicity islands are found in pathogenic bacteria but not in non-pathogenic strains of the same or related species.

FIGURE 2.13

Result of an experiment in which a laboratory culture of *E. coli* lacking a plasmid was exposed to bacteria carrying the plasmid. The graph shows the proportion of the original population subsequently found to carry the plasmid at various times after exposure to the 'infected' *E. coli*. Note that the time-scale is in minutes.

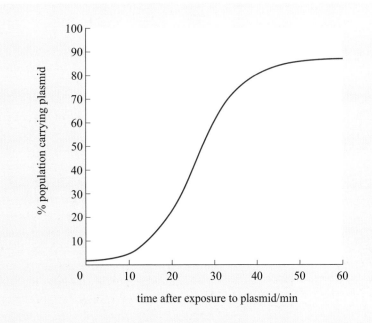

y-axis: % population carrying plasmid
x-axis: time after exposure to plasmid/min

Genes encoding important virulence factors may also be transferred to a bacterium, via a bacteriophage (a virus that infects bacteria – often abbreviated to phage), during lysogeny. Lysogeny occurs when an infecting bacteriophage does not replicate itself and move on, but instead incorporates its genome into that of its bacterial host. Phage infection cycles that result in lysogeny are described as **lysogenic**, and bacteria that harbour phage genomes in this way are known as **lysogens**. If the lysogenic phage carries a virulence factor gene, the lysogen may become pathogenic. The genes that encode the cholera toxin and the diphtheria toxin are both bacteriophage genes that are transferred to bacteria in this way.

2.4.1 Toxins

Toxins are broadly defined as substances of microbial origin that can damage the cells of another organism, at low concentrations. Toxins act at the level of the host. They are mainly associated with bacteria, but fungi also produce some potent toxins such as **aflatoxin**, and algal toxins are found in the poisonous algal blooms known as red tides. Toxins involved in infectious disease are predominantly associated with extracellular pathogens; intracellular pathogens such as viruses do not produce them.

Bacterial toxins are classified as either exotoxins or endotoxins, and have been the subject of intense research because of their importance as virulence factors. However, the role of toxins in pathogenesis is not always clear, as their behaviour *in vitro* can be very different from that observed *in vivo*. Sometimes, the toxin produced by an organism is responsible for the symptoms of the disease it causes. Such diseases can be described as **intoxications**(!), and the isolated toxin can produce the disease symptoms in the absence of the toxin-producing organism. An example of this is a toxin produced by *Clostridium botulinum*, which can give rise to botulism even if the organism itself is no longer present. The classic example of this is in undercooked meat products (*botulinum* comes from *botulus*, the Latin word for sausage), where the bacteria have been killed but the toxin has retained its activity.

Nearly all **exotoxins** are heat-labile (unstable at high temperatures), and lose their activity between 60 and 80 °C.

◯ Would you expect exotoxins to be heat-labile?

⬤ Yes. Most exotoxins are proteins, and these lose their structure, and hence their function, when they are heated.

Exotoxins are amongst the most toxic substances known: for example, an oral dose of 70 ug is a lethal dose for an 'average' person, and 5 g would be enough to kill everyone in the world! It is perhaps surprising, then, that this molecule, colloquially known as botox, is used (at *very* low doses) as an anti-wrinkle agent! The muscle paralysis caused by the exotoxin prevents facial muscles from wrinkling the skin, and also from creating any facial expression. Bacteria usually secrete exotoxins as they grow, causing a variety of effects in the animal host. Some toxins bind to surface receptors on host cells and initiate transmembrane signals. Other types of toxin damage membranes directly by disruption, or by the introduction of pores. Finally, there are exotoxins that target intracellular components, and comprise an enzyme that is translocated across the membrane. This last type of toxin conforms to the so-called **A–B model** of exotoxin structure, where A and B represent the different subunits observed in these toxins. A is the subunit responsible for the toxic effects once inside the cell, and B is the binding subunit which allows A entry into cells. The heat-labile toxins of enterotoxigenic *E. coli* (see below) have an A–B structure, and so does the neurotoxin tetanospasmin, produced by the Gram-positive bacillus *Clostridium tetani*. This toxin causes the muscle spasms of tetanus. (Note that tetanus is environmentally acquired, and is not a communicable disease.)

Endotoxins are components of the outer membrane of Gram-negative bacteria that are released during cell division and lysis, and indirectly induce fever in the host. Endotoxins are the lipopolysaccharide (LPS) molecules that take the place of phospholipids in the outer membrane.

○ Recall the mechanism of attachment of LPS to the outer membrane.

⬤ Attachment is via the fatty acyl chains of lipid A (Figure 2.7a).

It turns out that the lipid A part is important for the endotoxin activity. Lipid A and the attached LPS together stimulate macrophages to secrete a variety of cytokines (small proteins that act as signalling molecules) involved in inflammatory and immune responses, and LPS alone also activates the complement system. The resulting symptoms in the host are chiefly the fever and shock (a sudden drop in blood pressure), characteristic of so-called **endotoxic shock**, a serious condition with a high mortality. Endotoxic shock is a frequent complication of Gram-negative septicaemia, and is a clinically significant response by a patient to the presence of Gram-negative bacteria in the bloodstream.

Summary of Sections 2.2–2.4

1   Only a few bacteria are pathogenic, and not all cause disease in all host individuals.

2   The structures of different bacterial cell walls can be used as a basis for selective antibacterial therapy.

3   The pathogenicity of a bacterium depends on the virulence factors, often encoded in pathogenicity islands, that it can deploy.

4   Genes for virulence factors can be transmitted vertically, but of major clinical importance is horizontal transmission, which is mediated by plasmids, transposons, or bacteriophage.

5   A major virulence factor is the production of one or more toxins.

6   Exotoxins are secreted proteins that often have an A–B structure.

7   Endotoxins are bacterial surface components that can stimulate the immune system and cause symptoms of endotoxic shock.

2.5 The infection process

2.5.1 Gaining entry to the host

Bacteria may enter the human host by any of the routes described in Section 1.5. Infectious diseases are nearly always transmitted by vegetative (actively dividing) bacteria rather than by spores, with some notable exceptions such as anthrax, which can be spread by the **endospores** of *Bacillus anthracis* (see Figure 2.14).

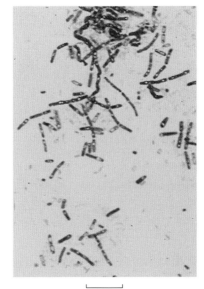

15 μm

FIGURE 2.14
Endospores of *Bacillus anthracis*. The culture was stained with hot malachite green and counterstained with safranin, which stains vegetative cells red and spores green. Some of the spores are still within the bacteria, but others are free.

Endospores are formed inside some bacteria, and are highly resistant structures capable of persisting in the environment, for example in soil, for extended periods of time. Most diseases contracted from spores are therefore acquired from the environment rather than from another person. For instance, tetanus, which is caused by the spores of *Clostridium tetani*, often results from the entry of soil into a skin wound (see above).

2.5.2 Adherence

Having gained entry to the host, the bacterium must attach itself to a host surface; if it fails to do so, it gets swept away or otherwise lost from the body. Attachment is a crucial step for any bacterium, irrespective of whether it will multiply on the host cell surface, invade the host tissues, or spread to other parts of the body. The bacterial and host cell surfaces are both negatively charged, and therefore actually repel one another. Bacteria have a whole range of structures external to the cell wall that aid in overcoming this repulsion and mediating adherence to the host.

Capsules are associated with virulence and can be important in adhesion. They can also protect the bacterium against drying and the action of detergents, and so prolong their persistence in the environment (Figure 2.15). Some staphylococci produce a loosely attached slime layer which, along with the teichoic acid component of their cell walls, allows them to stick to surfaces where other bacteria are swept away. These staphylococci are known as coagulase-negative staphylococci (this will be explained further below) and are not normally pathogenic, but when they stick to medical equipment, such as the insides of tubing, they can cause hospital acquired infections (see Book 1, Chapter 4). Sometimes the outermost layer of the bacterium's surface, a fibrous layer known as the **glycocalyx**, can also be involved in mediating attachment to the host (Figure 2.16).

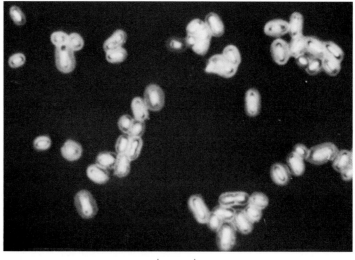

10 μm

FIGURE 2.15 *Klebsiella pneumoniae* stained to show its capsule.

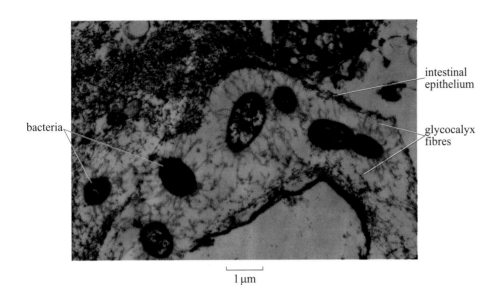

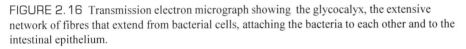

1 μm

FIGURE 2.16 Transmission electron micrograph showing the glycocalyx, the extensive network of fibres that extend from bacterial cells, attaching the bacteria to each other and to the intestinal epithelium.

Many bacteria have protein or polysaccharide molecules, called **adhesins**, on their surfaces, which bind to specific receptor molecules on the host cell membrane. The host receptors are the sugar chains of transmembrane glycoproteins, which are responsible for interactions between host cells and between these cells and the extracellular matrix. The type of glycoproteins found in a host cell membrane differs from cell to cell, and this is a significant factor in determining the type of cell a bacterium can adhere to.

 What is the clinical importance of this?

Diseases caused by particular bacteria will be confined, at least in the first instance, to particular tissues.

Fimbriae (singular: fimbria), found mostly on Gram-negative bacteria, are typically involved in adhesion, and are shown in Figure 2.17. These fine hair-like structures are also known as pili (singular: pilus), but some microbiologists reserve this term for the specialized structure known as a sex pilus, involved in bacterial conjugation (mating). There is a variety of fimbriae, distinguishable by their morphology, antigenic composition and receptor specificity. However, there are two main types: those whose function is inhibited *in vitro* by the sugar D-mannose, and those that remain unchanged in the presence of D-mannose.

What does inhibition by D-mannose indicate?

It suggests that the normal function of these fimbriae involves interaction with one or more mannose-like sugar residues on host cell surfaces.

FIGURE 2.17
Scanning electron micrograph of *Proteus vulgaris* showing long flagella and numerous shorter fimbriae.

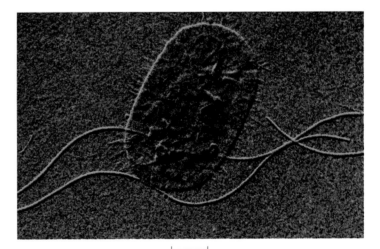

350 nm

Sometimes individual bacteria may express different fimbriae at different times, and it is thought that this property permits the use of alternative host targets for attachment.

Flagella (singular: flagellum) can act as adhesins, as in *Vibrio cholerae* infection, but the *motility* conferred by flagella can also be an important virulence factor. Flagella are highly antigenic and constitute the so-called H antigen of bacteria. H antigens may be used for **typing**, that is, establishing which strain of a bacterial species is associated with a particular outbreak of disease. An example is the use of H antigen typing to distinguish between different salmonella strains within the *Salmonella enterica* species (see Section 2.6.4 below). You will learn more about typing in Book 4.

Other adhesins include the **haemagglutinins**. Haemagglutinins are surface glycoproteins, with the ability to bind the membranes of red blood cells and cause agglutination (clumping). However, red blood cells share receptors with the respiratory epithelium, and it is the epithelial cells that are thought to be the most clinically significant target. *Bordetella pertussis* (Section 2.6.1) and *Helicobacter pylori* (Chapter 8) both employ haemagglutinins to mediate attachment.

○ Can you think of another infectious agent that uses a haemagglutinin for attachment?

● Influenza viruses have a haemagglutinin projecting from their envelopes. This protein is able to bind a variety of polysaccharides present on the surface of the host's respiratory epithelia (Book 1, Chapter 2 case study).

Other properties of the bacterial surface (such as the overall hydrophobicity of the cell exterior) can also play a part in attachment. Host proteins can be important too: fibronectin, an extracellular glycoprotein, may act as a receptor for pathogenic bacterial cells such as *Staphylococcus aureus* and *Treponema pallidum*, which are both known to bind it. Fibronectin is found in blood plasma and associated with mucosal cell surfaces, and its ability to bind bacteria is probably defensive, as it aids their elimination from the body.

2.5.3 Growth, multiplication and spread

As you saw in Chapter 1, once a bacterium has attached to the host it must obtain nutrients for growth and multiplication, and evade the host responses that have evolved to counter such bacteria. The pathogen also has to compete with the commensal flora for nutrients and available space. The bacterium may divide where it has attached, to form a local focus of infection, it may invade the underlying host tissues, or it may spread further afield via the blood or lymph systems. Unless it is especially virulent, a bacterium has a greater chance of success if it multiplies locally before spreading elsewhere.

Iron is an essential nutrient for bacteria, as a component of respiratory proteins such as cytochromes and many enzymes. The host tissues provide a rich medium for bacterial growth but iron is in short supply, as the serum concentration of free iron, at 10^{-18} moles per litre, is below that required for bacterial growth. Most of the iron in the host is in the form of Fe^{3+} – iron(III) – and is bound, both intracellularly and extracellularly, to specialized host proteins such as haem and transferrin. These iron-binding proteins therefore act as antibacterial factors, but pathogens have developed ways of dealing with them. Some bacteria secrete their own low-molecular-mass iron-binding proteins called **siderophores**, which have such a high affinity for iron that they can remove it from the host's iron-binding proteins. Bacteria that express siderophores also express new outer membrane proteins, which serve as receptors for the siderophores and their bound iron(III). Some bacteria, including *E. coli* and *Salmonella*, produce more than one siderophore, and salmonellae also have receptors for siderophores produced by other bacteria!

○ What advantage does this property confer?

● In a mixed population, the salmonellae are at a selective advantage because they can collect iron from several sources.

Neisseria meningitidis and *Neisseria gonorrhoeae* do not secrete siderophores, but have membrane-bound iron-binding proteins, which interact directly with those of the host.

○ Suggest a molecular explanation to account for the transfer of iron from a host iron-binding protein to a *Neisseria* one. (Don't attempt this if you haven't studied S204!)

● The affinity for iron of the *Neisseria* iron-binding protein must be greater than that of the host iron-binding protein, allowing the bound iron to pass from the host protein to the bacterial one.

Any bacterium growing in the host must also have fully functional biosynthetic pathways for aromatic amino acids, as these compounds are also scarce in the host tissues. These pathways are essential for bacterial production of folic acid, which is needed for DNA and RNA synthesis.

Having secured its nutritional requirements, the bacterium can begin to grow and divide. Under laboratory conditions, some potential pathogens, such as *E. coli*, have a doubling time of 20 minutes. Doubling times *in vivo* are usually longer, but many bacteria easily outstrip the shortest doubling time managed by cells of the host. The host cells with the shortest doubling time (6 hours) are the lymphocytes that mediate the adaptive immune response. Their doubling time is short, allowing the adaptive immune response to be launched as rapidly as possible (you will learn much more about immune responses in Book 3). Any delay gives the bacteria an advantage; the quicker that they can multiply and spread, the more likely it is that host tissues will be damaged and that disease will develop. It is a race between invader and defender, with the host's own tissues as the prize. Note that the disease caused by a bacterium is actually an unfortunate consequence of its primary evolutionary 'need' to multiply and move on to a new host. Sometimes a bacterium does not need to find a new host in order to persist, since it has populations established elsewhere. This can happen when a bacterium acquired from the environment causes an infection, but is not normally transmitted from person to person. This is the case with the bacillus that causes tetanus, *Clostridium tetani*, whose spores are abundant in soil.

All successful pathogens are able to evade the host immune response in some way. The innate immune system is the first line of defence, and phagocytes and the complement system are the main antibacterial components. Later on, the specific adaptive immune response comes into play, and antibodies that can bind bacteria and their products are produced. These antibodies label the bacteria for destruction by other immune system components, and may neutralize enzymes and toxins that the bacteria have made. You will learn more about the immune system and its response to pathogens in Book 3.

Many bacteria, particularly Gram-negative ones, cannot penetrate further than the epithelial layers. Here they grow and multiply, forming a thin layer or film on the epithelium where they have attached; for example, *Bordetella pertussis*, the organism that causes whooping cough, multiplies on the respiratory epithelium. These bacteria may cause diseases by expressing toxins or other virulence factors; for instance, the symptoms of diphtheria are caused by a toxin produced by Gram-positive *Corynebacterium diphtheriae*. If the epithelium is wet, it is very easy for bacteria to spread along it and form new foci of infection. The fluids covering the epithelia of the genitourinary tract and the conjunctiva of the eyes, and the continuous flow of the gut contents can facilitate the spread of bacteria. In respiratory tract infections, the mucociliary escalator provides the pathogens with new opportunities for infecting previously uninfected tissue. All of these flushing actions, which serve to sweep bacteria away, may sometimes allow them to spread further.

Few bacteria initiate infection on or via the skin, apart from those organisms specially adapted to this harsh environment. Spreading on the skin can occur, particularly when aided by the rubbing and scratching action of fingers and nails. Fingers are very efficient in spreading impetigo contagiosa, an acute skin infection caused by either staphylococci or streptococci. Probably the most infamous example of a rapidly spreading bacterial infection is necrotizing fasciitis, which is caused by a species of *Streptococcus*, the 'flesh-eating bacteria' of tabloid headlines (see Figure 2.18). The infection begins as a serious streptococcal skin infection and spreads to the subcutaneous tissues and blood. The resulting septicaemia can kill a patient very quickly, and the mortality is greater than 50%. The skin is also involved in many systemic bacterial infections that are initiated at other sites, such as syphilis, where there is a characteristic rash in the secondary stage of the disease.

FIGURE 2.18
Necrotizing fasciitis on the abdomen of a patient.

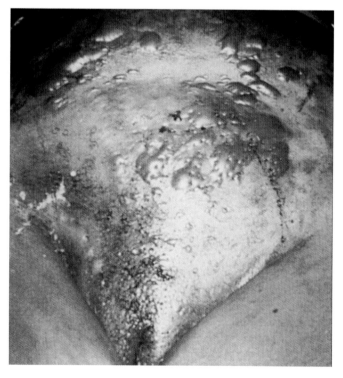

Some bacteria, e.g. *Salmonella, Mycobacteria* and *Chlamydia trachomatis*, are intracellular parasites, and have to gain entry to host cells in order to grow and multiply. There is less competition for resources inside host cells, and the bacterium is sheltered from complement proteins and antibodies. Uptake into the host cell may be accomplished by phagocytosis of the bacterium. If the cell is a macrophage or a polymorphonuclear leukocyte, the organism has to resist the intracellular killing mechanisms these cells employ. Thus the very cells that are meant to destroy bacteria, end up supporting their growth and multiplication. Sometimes the bacterium binds to specific receptors or components of the host cell surface, such as integrin proteins. These host proteins form a network around the host cell and mediate binding to other host cells and surfaces. The binding of an integrin to its target ligand can stimulate phagocytosis. The integrins recognize particular amino acid sequences on target molecules, and bacteria can mimic these sequences and bind instead, following which they can be phagocytosed. You will meet integrins again in Book 3.

- ○ Integrins recognize sequences in molecules. How can whole bacteria, many orders of magnitude bigger than single molecules, pass into the cell?

- ● Phagocytosis involves a relatively large area of the cell surface, not just a single integrin molecule and its ligand. The resulting phagosome is easily big enough to contain one or more bacteria.

In fact, many pathogens bypass phagosomes altogether and pass directly into the cytoplasm by a variety of methods, the description of which is beyond the scope of this text.

Some bacteria, having attached to the host, do invade beyond the epithelial layers. The first barrier they must overcome is the basement membrane, and once over this hurdle, the gel-like nature of the connective tissue matrix makes movement difficult. Bacteria have been found to produce a whole range of degradative enzymes such as proteinases, collagenases and hyaluronidases. *Staphylococcus aureus* has a particularly impressive array of such enzymes. Hyaluronidase has been known as 'spreading factor' in the past because it was believed to allow bacteria to spread through subepithelial tissues, by breaking down the hyaluronic acid component of the tissue matrix. However, the role of this and other degradative enzymes in pathogenesis is now less clear, and it is now thought that they may be involved in bacterial nutrition rather than spread. Infections can also spread directly within the body from wounds or existing foci of infection; for example, an infection in the appendix can spread to the abdominal cavity to cause peritonitis, a life-threatening condition.

Not all bacteria spread directly from the focus of infection on cell layers or within them, but instead exploit the host transport systems of lymph and blood vessels to spread further afield. Using these systems, a bacterium may spread right through the body in a few days, resulting in a **systemic infection** in which the whole body is involved. Most microbes entering the subepithelial tissues end up in the lymph and are carried to a local lymph node, where they are phagocytosed by macrophages within the node. The subepithelial layers in the lung, mouth and nasopharynx (back of the throat) are particularly well supplied with lymph vessels. The lymph continually washes any foreign bodies from the tissues to the lymph nodes for disposal, but not all bacteria are eliminated so easily. Some bacteria even manage to grow in the nodes, which then disseminate the infection further, while others escape in the lymph leaving the node, and may eventually reach the bloodstream. One such enterprising microbe is *Yersinia pestis*, the causative agent of plague.

Although the blood would seem to provide the ideal vehicle for the spread of bacteria, in fact few of them regularly invade this system, and those that do are responsible for serious diseases. Examples of bacteria that do spread via the bloodstream include *Salmonella typhi* and *Bacillus anthracis* (these organisms cause typhoid fever and anthrax respectively). However, many other bacteria do *invade* the bloodstream, causing transient **bacteraemia** (the presence of bacteria in the blood); their fate is usually to be rapidly cleared in the liver and spleen by the macrophages of the **mononuclear phagocyte system**, formerly called the reticuloendothelial system. The mononuclear phagocyte system is a collection of phagocytic macrophages, found in the blood and tissues, that trap and eliminate particles foreign to the body. Transient bacteraemia can cause disease if the host is immunocompromised, or if the bacteria reach particularly vulnerable areas: for example, staphylococci reaching the bones can cause osteomyelitis (inflammation of the bone marrow) if the bone is damaged. Bacteria that are intracellular parasites can spread only by using the blood, lymph or a mobile cell such as a macrophage to transport them. The blood may also transport bacterial products such as toxins to distant targets, as is found in some diphtheria infections when the spread of the exotoxin from the site of primary infection (the throat) can give rise to systemic symptoms.

Bacteria do not generally use nerves as a means of spread, but blood-borne bacteria sometimes reach the cerebrospinal fluid and go on to invade the brain or spinal cord. Examples of this strategy are found in *Neisseria meningitidis* and *Mycobacterium tuberculosis*, both of which can cause meningitis.

2.5.4 Asymptomatic carriers

An asymptomatic carrier has already been described as an individual who harbours a pathogen but does not develop any disease that the pathogen causes. This is just one of several types of asymptomatic carrier. An infected person who *does* go on to develop clinical disease may appear healthy but actually be a source of infection for others; for example, a person with syphilis may have no symptoms in the early stages of the disease. Alternatively, an individual who has recovered from a disease may still carry large numbers of the causative pathogen, which can be transmitted to others. For instance, the causative bacteria of diphtheria or whooping cough may persist in the nasopharynx for months following recovery.

Carriers are important sources of infection in the community, and by their very nature are difficult to identify. Perhaps the most infamous carrier was a cook called Mary Mallon, who lived in New York at the beginning of the last century. She had recovered from typhoid fever, but still harboured the bacterium that caused it, and shed it in her faeces. 'Typhoid Mary', as she was nicknamed is believed to have been the source of infection for at least 53 cases of typhoid fever.

Summary of Section 2.5

1   Diseases may be caused by vegetative bacteria (most commonly), endospores (in a few cases) or occasionally toxins.

2   Once a bacterium has gained entry to a host, it must adhere to it. This is facilitated by external structures such as capsules, sticky molecules called adhesins, or projections such as fimbriae. These adhesion devices all anchor the bacterium to a host-cell receptor molecule.

3   Adherent bacteria have a range of strategies for amassing materials for growth and division. When sufficiently large numbers are established, the pathogen can spread within the host.

4   Bacteria are adapted to evade host immune responses.

5   Some individuals carry and disseminate pathogens without showing signs of the disease themselves.

2.6 Types of bacterial infection

In this section, bacterial infections are classified according to their mode of transmission, and selected examples of each type are used to illustrate the principles introduced in the above sections.

2.6.1 Airborne infections

Diphtheria

Diphtheria is an acute, contagious disease of the respiratory tract caused by the Gram-positive rod, *Corynebacterium diphtheriae*. Not all strains of *C. diphtheriae* are pathogenic, only those that produce a toxin, known as diphtheria toxin (DT). The *tox* gene, carried by a lysogenic bacteriophage, encodes this toxin. Only those bacteria that are lysogens for bacteriophage containing the *tox* gene can produce the diphtheria toxin, and it is this toxin that is responsible for the symptoms of diphtheria. As you saw above, iron is limiting in mammalian tissues, yet low levels of iron actually *increase* the production of diphtheria toxin. One subunit of DT binds to cell surface receptors, with the result that the whole toxin is taken up by endocytosis (invagination of the cell membrane). Once inside a vesicle, the toxin is cleaved and the products released into the cytosol. One product is an enzyme that inactivates an elongation factor essential for protein synthesis. Without this elongation factor, protein synthesis is inhibited and the cell dies. The death and destruction of epithelial tissue is thought to facilitate the bacterial infection process.

◯ What kind of structure does DT have?

⬤ It has an A–B model structure. The subunit that binds to host-cell receptors and mediates toxin uptake is the B subunit, and the enzyme is the A subunit.

Diphtheria begins as a sore throat following an incubation period of 2–6 days. The bacteria multiply in the throat and cause an inflammatory reaction in the upper respiratory tract. There is mild fever, and an offensive exudate is produced which forms a layer on the respiratory mucosa, known as a pseudomembrane, shown in Figure 2.19. The pseudomembrane is the result of tissue damage by the toxin, and can end up blocking the airway, leading to asphyxiation and even death. The lymph system becomes congested and fails to drain the neck area, which swells as a result, producing a characteristic 'bullneck' appearance.

FIGURE 2.19
Pseudomembrane (shown by arrows) in a child with diphtheria.

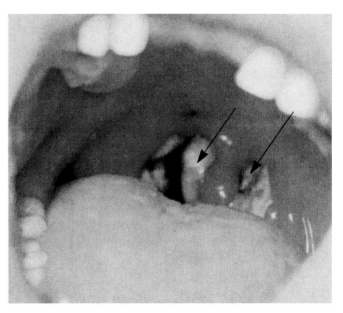

The corynebacteria are essentially confined to the throat epithelium by the host defences, but, as you saw above, the toxin they produce is able to reach other parts of the body. The heart, kidneys and peripheral nerve tissues are the most common targets. In infections where the airway remains clear, toxin-mediated damage to the heart is the most common cause of death.

Treatment of diphtheria is initially concerned with maintaining a clear airway, so that the patient can breathe. Intubation (introduction of a tube into the throat via the mouth) or even tracheotomy (cutting the windpipe) might be necessary. Removal of the pseudomembrane is difficult surgically, as cutting can cause excessive bleeding and further damage. The key factor in recovery from diphtheria is the antibody response. Antibodies that bind the diphtheria toxin are able to neutralize it, and these antibodies are therefore called **antitoxins**. If the toxin is neutralized, recovery is possible even if the bacteria persist. Penicillin and erythromycin (a macrolide antibiotic, see Table 2.1) are the drugs of choice for killing the diphtheria bacteria.

◯ Recall the action of penicillin.

⬤ It prevents peptidoglycan synthesis.

Other members of the genus *Corynebacterium*, sometimes called diphtheroids, are common commensals of the eye and nasopharynx. It is not surprising then that *Corynebacterium diphtheriae* can persist for long periods in the nasopharynx, following recovery from diphtheria. If this occurs, the host becomes a carrier and sheds large numbers of bacteria into the immediate environment (see above). The bacteria are resistant to drying and can remain viable for long periods in surface dust. Carriers are probably the main source of infection with *C. diphtheriae* for non-immune individuals.

Humans are the only species for which *C. diphtheriae* is pathogenic and infection brings about lasting immunity. Vaccination programmes have been very successful in eradicating diphtheria from developed countries. In England and Wales in 1914, there were 5863 deaths from diphtheria infections. Mass immunization began in 1942, and by 1957 only four deaths from diphtheria infections were recorded. In developing countries, where resources for such programmes are unavailable, it has been a different story (see the map of diphtheria hotspots in the Book 2 online resources). Children become susceptible as they lose their passively acquired maternal antibodies at around three months of age, and are the group with the highest incidence of infection. Diphtheria spreads most easily where living conditions are crowded, so is more common among the poor. In areas where vaccination programmes have kept the disease under control, it can re-emerge if social and political upheavals occur. This was demonstrated most recently in the states of the former Soviet Union, where the collapse of communism led to a disruption in vaccination programmes – in 1994 there were nearly 50 000 cases of diphtheria and 1750 deaths from the disease in the former Soviet states.

Pertussis (whooping cough)

Pertussis, or whooping cough, is a contagious disease of the respiratory tract caused by the Gram-negative coccobacillus (a bacillus that is so short it almost looks like a coccus) *Bordetella pertussis*. Initially, the disease resembles the common cold, but soon mucus is produced in such quantities that the airways become temporarily blocked. A succession of violent coughs, known as paroxysms, are needed to clear the mucus. Once the mucus has been cleared, air is sucked into the lungs in a characteristic 'whoop', which gives the disease its name. *Bordetella pertussis* produces several toxins, and these cause the symptoms of whooping cough.

The bacterium is transmitted by droplet infection and inhaled into the trachea and bronchi. Colonization of these surfaces is facilitated by a haemagglutinin known as filamentous haemagglutinin (FHA). FHA binds to specific molecules on the surfaces of ciliated epithelial cells of the respiratory mucosa. Colonization is further aided by the presence of fimbriae and an outer membrane protein, pertactin, and *Bordetella pertussis* is also able to grow in the macrophages that line the alveoli. FHA and the toxin pertussigen (see below) act together to get the bacterium taken up into the macrophage. The subsequent killing of the phagocytosed bacterium is prevented by another *Bordetella pertussis* toxin, known as adenylate cyclase toxin.

The main toxin produced by *B. pertussis* is pertussis toxin (PTx) or pertussigen, which has a number of toxic effects on the host. These include increased sensitivity to histamine, overproduction of insulin and subsequent hypoglycaemia (low blood sugar), and an increase in leukocyte numbers. *B. pertussis* also produces a tracheal cytotoxin that kills the ciliated epithelial cells. The copious mucus produced during pertussis further impedes ciliary action, and the impaired mucociliary escalator leaves patients with paroxysms as the only means to clear their airways. The bacterium effectively disables a major line of defence, inhibiting its own removal and allowing further infection.

Treatment of whooping cough is difficult. The antibiotics erythromycin and ampicillin (a penicillin derivative) may reduce the severity of the disease if given before the paroxysmal stage, but have little effect once the infection is well established. *Bordetella pertussis* is pathogenic only in humans and recovery from infection brings lasting immunity. As with diphtheria, successful vaccination programmes have essentially eradicated whooping cough from many developed countries. However, in countries where such immunization programmes are not possible, such as countries in the developing world, pertussis remains a leading cause of death. Every year, around 360 000 children, most of them under the age of five, die of whooping cough.

2.6.2 Arthropod-borne infections

Bubonic plague

Bubonic plague has been one of the most terrifying infectious diseases in history. In the 14th century it swept across Europe from Asia as the Black Death, killing around a quarter of the European population. It is caused by the Gram-negative coccobacillus *Yersinia pestis,* which is actually a rodent pathogen (Figure 2.20). In the Black Death, fleas living as parasites on black rats (*Rattus rattus*) infected with *Y. pestis* picked up the bacteria while feeding on rat blood. They then transferred the disease to humans while feeding on human blood. In the gut of a flea harbouring *Y. pestis,* the bacterium multiplies to such an extent that the gut becomes obstructed. This blockage causes the flea to regurgitate some of its gut contents, which contain the bacterium, during the next blood meal. *Y. pestis* is also spread from person to person by human fleas, and probably body lice.

Around the insect bite, the lymph system is affected, leading to inflammation of the lymph glands. This eventually produces painful swellings, called buboes, in the groin, armpits or neck. The buboes give bubonic plague its name.

○ Suggest what determines the location of the buboe.

● The location of the bite. The local lymph nodes draining the bite site will be most rapidly affected. Thus a bite on the leg will give rise initially to groin buboes.

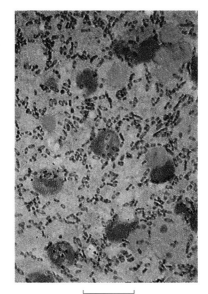

10 μm

FIGURE 2.20
Yersinia pestis, the cause of bubonic plague, in a sample of liver; the preparation is stained with Leishman's stain.

45

The bacterium can move into other tissues from the buboes, including the lungs. This gives rise to the so-called pneumonic plague, a severe and highly contagious form of bronchopneumonia spread by droplet infection (the nursery rhyme line 'Atishoo, atishoo, we all fall down' refers to this illness!). This means that plague does not remain a zoonotic disease (a disease naturally transmitted from other vertebrates to a human host), but can rapidly spread from person to person. During a plague infection, the bacteria can also end up multiplying in the blood, giving so-called septicaemic plague.

Yersinia pestis is one of the most deadly bacteria and it has a formidable array of virulence factors. It attaches to receptors on the host cells by an adhesin known as Myf/pH6 antigen, and then introduces plasmid-encoded toxic proteins into the host cytosol. The plasmid expressing these proteins is a 70 kb (kilobases) virulence plasmid, and the proteins are encoded by a region termed the *Yop* virulon. The Yop proteins determine bacterial resistance to phagocytosis by host macrophages and polymorphonuclear leukocytes, induce apoptosis (programmed cell death) in macrophages, and inhibit cytokine release.

☐ How would Yop protein activity affect the host's immune response?

⬤ The immune response would be severely limited.

If *Yersinia* is phagocytosed, it can still grow in the phagolysosome (the vesicle formed by fusion of the phagosome with a lysosome), but it is essentially an extracellular parasite. Another important *Yersinia* virulence factor is a chromosomally-encoded siderophore known as yersiniabactin, which contributes to the accumulation of large quantities of iron-containing molecules from the host.

☐ *Yersinia* is Gram-negative: what other toxic molecule would you expect to be present in plague victims?

⬤ The cell wall component endotoxin, or LPS, which can cause endotoxic shock.

The plague symptoms of high fever and vascular damage leading to subcutaneous haemorrhages that turn the skin black (hence 'Black Death'), correspond to those caused by endotoxin, but in fact it is unlikely that these symptoms are caused by endotoxin alone. Other *Yersinia* toxins are thought to produce this severe systemic disease, but their actions are not fully understood.

The plague bacterium is still a threat: natural rodent populations in many parts of the world harbour *Yersinia pestis,* and the situation in rats is constantly monitored. The bacterium is sensitive to a number of antibiotics, including tetracycline, and if this is given early in the course of bubonic plague, recovery is possible. Septicaemic plague is always fatal, pneumonic plague is usually fatal and untreated bubonic plague can have a mortality as high as 50%. A vaccine is available but the immunity conferred is short-lived.

2.6.3 Direct-contact infections

Staphylococcal infections

The staphylococci are Gram-positive cocci that occur in characteristic grape-like clusters, as shown in Figure 2.21. They are part of the normal flora of the upper respiratory tract, skin, intestine and vagina. Infection with staphylococci may be endogenous, but direct contact is the most important mode of transmission as they are found mainly on the exterior of humans and animals. Staphylococci, especially *Staphylococcus aureus,* are some of the most important human pathogens and produce a large number of enzymes and toxins that allow them to invade, spread and multiply in their hosts (Table 2.2). They are the most common cause of skin infections such as boils, styes and impetigo contagiosa (Figure 2.22, overleaf), are important in wound infection, and can spread in the lymph and blood to affect almost any organ or tissue and produce internal abscesses. Since most staphylococcal infections involve the formation of pus, they are classified as pyogenic (pus-forming) cocci.

Pathogenic staphylococci can be distinguished from non-pathogenic strains by their ability to produce the enzyme coagulase, but coagulase-negative staphylococci can also cause hospital acquired infections (Book 1, Chapter 4).

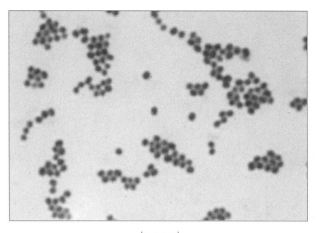

(a) 20 µm

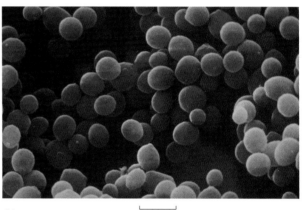

(b) 4 µm

FIGURE 2.21 *Staphylococcus.* (a) Gram-stained smear. (b) Scanning electron micrograph. Note that the cells occur in clusters.

TABLE 2.2 Some virulence factors of *Staphylococcus aureus*.

Virulence factors	Activity
protein A	interferes with normal binding of IgG antibody
fibronectin-binding protein	binds fibronectin on host cells
α-, β-, γ- and δ-haemolysins	destroy erythrocytes; additionally, α-haemolysin damages skin and β-haemolysin attacks nerves
Panton–Valentine leukocidin	damages phagocytic leukocytes
toxin A, toxin B	exfoliative toxins
enterotoxins (general term for toxins that act on the mucosal cells of the gut)	induce the vomiting and diarrhoea experienced with staphylococcal food poisoning
toxic shock syndrome toxin-1	associated with the fever and shock of toxic shock syndrome*
coagulase	cleaves fibrinogen in blood plasma to give fibrin
hyaluronidase (spreading factor)	breaks down hyaluronic acid in connective tissue
proteases	degrade proteins
lipases	break down lipids
deoxyribonucleases	degrade DNA

* A type of endotoxic shock that occurs in women and is caused by staphylococcal infection of the genital tract.

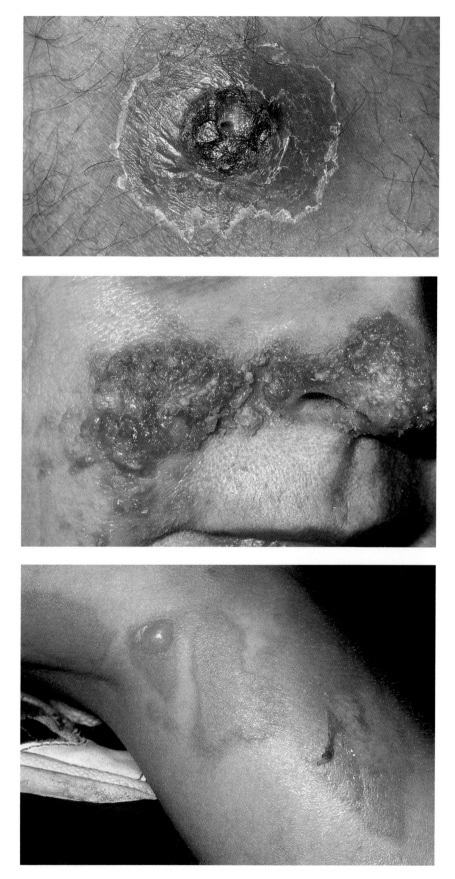

FIGURE 2.22
Staphylococcal skin infections. (a) A boil on the upper thigh of a patient; this infection arises when a large abscess forms around a hair follicle. (b) Impetigo contagiosa on a woman's nose and cheek. (c) Scalded skin syndrome seen on the leg of a child. Reddened areas of skin (centre) peel off, leaving 'scalded'-looking, moist areas (upper left).

☐ From the name, suggest what coagulase does.

⬤ Coagulase probably acts in the blood clotting (coagulation) cascade.

In fact, coagulase converts prothrombin, a precursor in the blood clotting mechanism, to an active complex that cleaves fibrinogen to give a fibrin clot. As well as forming clots, the fibrin can also coat the surface of staphylococci, protecting them from phagocytosis. Phagocytosis is further resisted by the action of the enzyme catalase, which breaks down hydrogen peroxide to water and oxygen. Hydrogen peroxide is produced in macrophages and kills the microbes that they have phagocytosed, so the synthesis of catalase allows staphylococci to resist this killing mechanism. Additional factors for resisting phagocytosis are Panton–Valentine leukocidin (leukocidins are extracellular toxins that may kill phagocytic leukocytes) and a cell surface protein called protein A, which can bind host antibodies by their non-antigen-binding ends.

☐ How might the fibrin coating protect the bacteria?

⬤ The bacteria are effectively hidden behind a layer of host molecules, so escape the immune response.

Other virulence factors, such as proteases, nucleases and lipases, have a less clear-cut role in pathogenesis, and may simply be involved in bacterial metabolism.

Two exotoxins with an obvious pathogenic effect are the **exfoliative** or epidermolytic toxins known as toxin A and toxin B (not to be confused with the A and B subunits of A–B model toxins). These plasmid-borne virulence factors are responsible for the symptoms of staphylococcal scalded skin syndrome (Figure 2.22c), where the epidermis (the outer layer of the skin) becomes detached and sloughs off (exfoliates). The underlying skin is left red and raw as though it has been scalded, hence the name. This disease is seen most often in children, and can be fatal for newborns due to the accompanying fluid loss. Another staphylococcal virulence factor that has been recognized recently is toxic shock syndrome toxin-1, produced by *Staphylococcus aureus*. This toxin causes toxic shock syndrome, whose symptoms include vascular shock and fever, and can be fatal.

Staphylococcal infections are usually treated with β-lactam antibiotics such as methicillin and cephalosporins (Table 2.1). In recent years, however, methicillin-resistant *Staphylococcus aureus,* or MRSA, has become a problem, leading to the use of vancomycin as a 'last resort' antibiotic therapy.

Chlamydial infections

Three species of chlamydiae are pathogenic for humans: *Chlamydia trachomatis, C. pneumoniae* and *C. psittaci.* The chlamydiae resemble viruses in that they are obligate intracellular parasites (i.e. cannot live outside the host cell), they have a similar replication cycle (outlined in Figure 2.23) and they are dependent on their host cell for energy, since they cannot catabolize substances to produce ATP. However, unlike viruses, they can synthesize their own macromolecules. Chlamydiae are a type of Gram-negative bacteria, even though they do not have a peptidoglycan cell wall.

☐ In the absence of peptidoglycan, how can *Chlamydia* be classified as Gram-negative?

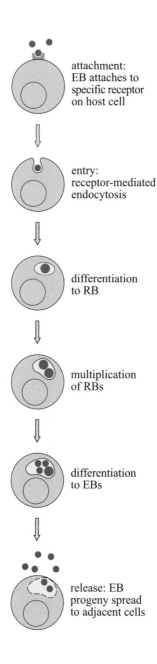

attachment:
EB attaches to
specific receptor
on host cell

entry:
receptor-mediated
endocytosis

differentiation
to RB

multiplication
of RBs

differentiation
to EBs

release: EB
progeny spread
to adjacent cells

Either by the presence of other Gram-negative features (such as an outer membrane) or by molecular sequence comparisons.

Chlamydia trachomatis is a major human pathogen that causes eye diseases and infections of the genital tract. The bacterium is contracted as a so-called elementary body, which is metabolically inactive. The elementary bodies are taken up into cells by phagocytosis or pinocytosis, and differentiate into structures known as reticulate bodies. Reticulate bodies are metabolically active but not infectious; they produce more infectious elementary bodies, which leave the cell when it lyses.

Chlamydia trachomatis causes trachoma, one of the longest-known infectious diseases. This infection, which damages the eyes and can result in blindness, is endemic in North Africa, Asia and South America. The elementary bodies are deposited on the conjunctiva by flies, fingers or towels, resulting in conjunctivitis. Healing is usually spontaneous; but over the course of 25–30 years, repeated re-infections and secondary infections can lead to blindness, as scar tissue accumulates on the cornea (Figure 2.24). This terrible disease is best prevented by basic improvements in hygiene, such as the provision of clean water. Once infection is established, it can be treated with tetracycline antibiotics. These simple measures could alleviate the suffering of the estimated 500 million people with trachoma, but are beyond the means of most of the countries where the disease is endemic. You can see how one charity is trying to help trachoma sufferers by looking at their website (see the Sight Savers International website in the Book 2 online resources).

FIGURE 2.23
The life cycle of *Chlamydia*. The free-living form of this bacterium (the elementary body, EB) binds to specific receptors on the epithelial cell surface and enters the cell by receptor-mediated endocytosis (RME). Normally, RME is followed by fusion of the endocytic vesicle with a lysosome and digestion of the contents, but this process is inhibited and instead the EB form differentiates into another form (reticulate body, RB) which divides to produce intracellular RB progeny. These RB *Chlamydia* differentiate into the EB form again, and after being released from the host cell go on to infect and destroy more cells in the same way.

FIGURE 2.24
An eye with trachoma. The conjunctiva is thickened, and inflammatory nodules lie on top of it.

In developed countries, *Chlamydia trachomatis* is best known as a sexually transmissible pathogen which causes so-called chlamydia infections. These infections may be asymptomatic, or cause inflammation of the urethra with itching and discharge. In women, a severe infection called pelvic inflammatory disease may develop that can lead to sterility. Newborn babies' eyes can become infected with *C. trachomatis* during birth, if the mother is harbouring a genital infection. The disease that develops is known as inclusion conjunctivitis. Adults too can acquire inclusion conjunctivitis, usually by transferring material from their own infected genital tracts to their eyes. Although unpleasant, these infections usually heal, even without treatment. Note that the different diseases caused by *Chlamydia trachomatis* are the result of infection with different strains of the organism.

2.6.4 Food- and water-borne infections

Salmonella infections

Salmonellae are Gram-negative rods found naturally in the intestines of many animals and birds (Figure 2.25). They cause two types of disease in humans: so-called enteric fevers and gastrointestinal infections (see below). The taxonomy of salmonellae is complicated, since every strain was originally regarded as a new species. As the various strains only differ from one another slightly in the structures of their O and H antigens (Section 2.2), the practice of referring to them as species has been abandoned. All salmonellae are now regarded as one species known as *Salmonella enterica,* which has a number of subspecies that are further divided into **serovars** or **serotypes**. A serovar is a variety identifiable only by its reaction with test sera (singular: serum) containing a range of antibodies. Worldwide, over 2000 serovars that cause human infections are recognized, with most infections in mammals due to *S. enterica* subspecies 1.

Salmonella food poisoning, or salmonellosis, results from the consumption of food contaminated with the bacterium. As few as 100 organisms or as many as 10^7 may be needed to cause an infection.

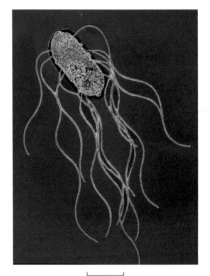

2 μm

FIGURE 2.25
Electron micrograph of *Salmonella*, showing a profusion of flagella.

○ Suggest reasons for this difference.

● The reasons may lie in the virulence factors carried by particular serovars, and/or in differences in the host's immune status or genetic make-up. Another reason may be that some bacteria are shielded from the acid environment of the stomach by being inside particles of food.

Salmonellae are able to resist the acid environment and proteases of the stomach. They are highly motile, and subsequently colonize the ileum (part of the small intestine). Some bacteria can attach to the microvilli of the intestinal epithelium by adhesins that bind to mannose-containing receptors on the host cells. The bacteria then cause localized degeneration of the cell membrane, until this barrier is breached, allowing the salmonellae to enter the cells. The bacteria then multiply in the epithelial cells, but do not penetrate further. You can see how salmonellae infect cells by watching the animation from the Book 2 online resources.

The symptoms of salmonellosis begin 15–48 hours after consuming contaminated food, once the bacteria have had time to multiply and reach a number sufficient to cause host cell damage. The infection is not serious in healthy individuals, who typically recover in 5–7 days, but serious complications can arise in the very old, the very young and the immunocompromised. Annually, around 3 million people worldwide die of salmonellosis. Once recovery has occurred, salmonellae may persist in the intestine and be carried asymptomatically. In contrast to most infectious diseases, salmonellosis is more of a problem in developed countries than developing ones. In developed countries, large-scale intensive farming of livestock and commercial food-processing provide much better opportunities for contamination than the small-scale enterprises of developing countries.

Enteric fevers are invasive infections of the salmonella serovars *Salmonella typhi* and *Salmonella paratyphi*, which cause typhoid fever and paratyphoid fever respectively. The fevers result from the consumption of contaminated food or water. In typhoid fever, once colonization of the ileum has occurred, the bacteria spread to lymphoid tissue, the blood, liver and gall bladder. Unlike salmonellosis, the mortality is high (up to 20%) in untreated cases. In the past, epidemics of typhoid fever occurred the world over, but the disease is now limited to areas where sanitation is poor. Paratyphoid fever resembles typhoid fever, but is less serious and has a lower mortality. You will learn more about enteric fevers in Book 3.

Travellers' diarrhoea

Many visitors abroad experience episodes of diarrhoea, and the *E. coli* bacterium is one major cause of such illnesses. Travellers become infected after consuming food or drink that has been prepared with contaminated water. In many countries, especially in the developing world, clean water is in short supply. The best way to prevent travellers' diarrhoea is to follow the maxim 'cook it, peel it, or forget it'. The local adult population is immune to such infections as a result of previous illnesses caused by these bacteria, but such illnesses are an everyday part of childhood.

The *E. coli* that cause diarrhoea are divided into six groups, each with its own characteristics:

> enterotoxigenic *E. coli* (ETEC);
>
> enteropathogenic *E. coli* (EPEC);
>
> enteroinvasive *E. coli* (EIEC);
>
> enteroaggregative *E. coli* (EAggEC);
>
> diffusely adherent *E. coli* (DAEC); and
>
> enterohaemorrhagic *E. coli* (EHEC).

These names are based on the main activity of the strains concerned, as explained below. (We do not expect you to memorize the differences.)

ETEC do not penetrate the gut epithelial cells, but mediate their effect via two toxins known as heat-stable toxin and heat-labile toxin. The genes encoding both these toxins and other virulence factors that allow the bacterium to colonize the intestine, usually reside on a plasmid. The heat-labile toxin binds specific gangliosides. Gangliosides are important components of receptor sites on cell membrane surfaces, and binding of the toxin to gangliosides on the epithelial cell surface activates the membrane-bound adenylate cyclase enzyme. Adenylate cyclase increases cyclic AMP production, and this causes an increase in the efflux of Na^+ and Cl^- ions from the cell and results in diarrhoea. Cholera toxin also produces diarrhoea by this mechanism (see Cholera Case Study). In a similar manner, the heat-stable toxin binds to a glycoprotein cell surface receptor that is coupled to the guanylate cyclase enzyme. As a result of this binding, the enzyme increases cyclic GMP production, which also causes diarrhoea.

EPEC are also non-invasive, but attach to the microvilli of the small intestine and destroy them. This type of *E. coli* is particularly associated with childhood diarrhoeal episodes in developing countries. You can watch how these bacteria attach to the small intestine by viewing the animation from the Book 2 online resources.

EIEC are able to invade gut epithelial cells and multiply inside them. Their invasive ability is conferred by a large plasmid.

EAggEC are so called because they form clumps on the epithelial cell surfaces.

DAEC get their name because they attach all over these cell surfaces. They particularly affect children who are malnourished or have immature immune systems.

EHEC cause haemorrhagic colitis and haemolytic uraemic syndrome and are dealt with below (Section 2.7.1).

Treatment for diarrhoea is largely a case of restoring the fluid and electrolyte balance disturbed by the disease. This is achieved most simply by oral rehydration therapy with sugar and salt in clean water. Rehydration therapy is especially important in children since they can rapidly become dangerously dehydrated.

Staphylococcal food poisoning

Exotoxins produced by *Staphylococcus aureus* cause the most common type of food poisoning seen in the UK and USA. Six heat-stable enterotoxins (see Table 2.2) have been identified that can resist temperatures up to 100 °C for a few minutes. Staphylococcal food poisoning is an intoxication, requiring just microgram quantities of the toxins to be consumed to produce the symptoms of nausea and vomiting.

○ The onset of symptoms of staphylococcal food poisoning is rapid (1–8 hours). Why?

● Because the bacteria themselves do not have to multiply to produce the disease, or even be present.

The toxins are produced by the cocci as they grow in food contaminated by incorrect handling or storage, e.g. inadequate refrigeration. Some people, known as shedders, release exceptionally large numbers of staphylococci from their nostrils and skin, and can pose a risk if they handle food, such as by making sandwiches. Fortunately, the symptoms of staphylococcal food poisoning do not last long (about 24 hours), and serious complications are rare in otherwise healthy individuals.

Summary of Section 2.6

1 Pathogens can be transmitted by air, arthropods, direct contact, or food and water.

2 Major airborne pathogens include diphtheria and pertussis.

3   Diphtheria symptoms are caused by a toxin that has a classic A–B structure and affects protein synthesis. *Corynebacterium* grows inside macrophages.

4   Pertussis symptoms are also caused by toxins, one of which inhibits the mucociliary escalator.

5   Both diphtheria and pertussis can be controlled by vaccination.

6   A major arthropod-borne disease is bubonic plague, caused by *Yersinia pestis*, which has many virulence factors encoded in the *Yop* virulon.

7   Major diseases spread by direct contact include staphylococcal infections and chlamydial infections.

8   *Staphylococcus* spp. produce many toxins and other virulence factors that enable them to resist phagocytosis and proliferate. Antibiotic resistance is an increasing problem with MRSA.

9   *Chlamydia* spp. are intracellular pathogens and cause urinogenital infections and eye disease.

10 Pathogens contracted through contaminated food include *Salmonella*, *E. coli* and *Staphylococcus*. All cause diarrhoea, and there may be further complications.

11 *Salmonella* strains grow within intestinal epithelial cells, and so do some types of *E. coli*. Other types of *E. coli* and *Staphylococcus* cause disease by toxin production.

CASE STUDY

You may now like to make a start on the two case studies that relate to this book.

The Tuberculosis Case Study consists of a CD entitled *Tuberculosis*, and accompanying Study Notes, which you will study at two main points in the course – both here, and again in Book 7. For now, we ask you to concentrate on the basic features of tuberculosis; you will return later to the strategies used to combat this disease.

The Cholera Case Study is text-based and also involves the use of online resources. Here you will learn the basics about the cholera organism and the disease that it causes.

2.7 New diseases

The majority of the infectious diseases that are familiar to us have been infecting human beings for centuries, if not millennia. The first documented reports of the Black Death date from the Middle Ages, and there are even recognizable descriptions of infectious diseases in Ancient Egyptian papyri. However, evolution is a continuing process, and we should not be surprised to learn that 'new' diseases are emerging all the time. You will learn more of the evolution of infectious diseases in Book 5, but here we describe two of the recently emerged bacterial ones. The first is a food-borne infection; the second is an insect-borne zoonosis.

2.7.1 *E. coli* O157

E. coli O (O antigen) 157 causes haemorrhagic colitis and haemolytic uraemic syndrome (HUS). This organism was first recognized in 1982 in the USA, but is now known throughout the world. Haemorrhagic colitis is a severe bloody diarrhoea, while HUS begins as diarrhoea, but develops into haemolytic anaemia (anaemia resulting from the destruction of red blood cells) and renal failure. Haemorrhagic colitis and HUS are associated with a variety of foods, such as undercooked hamburger meat, unpasteurized milk and fruit juices. Meat pies from a Lanarkshire butcher were responsible for the best-known UK episode involving *E. coli* O157 (Figure 2.26). The infectious dose is low, with estimates varying from 10–500 organisms, and children and elderly people are particularly at risk. Infection with *E. coli* O157 can be life-threatening in these age groups, especially in the case of HUS, which is a major cause of renal failure in children.

E. coli O157 has a number of virulence factors, including unusually high acid resistance, a haemolysin and specific structures for intestinal adherence. It also produces toxins known as verotoxins, which are very similar to toxins produced by the dysentery-causing bacteria of the genus *Shigella*. These *E. coli* toxins, sometimes referred to as shiga-like toxins because of this resemblance, are believed to kill cells of the vascular endothelium (lining of the blood vessels).

FIGURE 2.26
The butcher's shop in Wishaw, Lanarkshire, where the November 1996 outbreak of *E. coli* O157 food poisoning began.

2.7.2 Lyme disease

Lyme disease was first recognized in the Connecticut town of Lyme in 1975, and is a major new infectious disease in the USA. In the 1990s, there were 10 000 cases each year in the USA, a figure exceeded only by AIDS patients. The disease is also known in Europe, Asia and Australia, and is usually associated with forested areas. Lyme disease is caused by a spirochaete bacterium called *Borrelia burgdorferi* (Figure 2.27a overleaf), which infects deer and mice. The bacterium is transferred to humans by the bite of *Ixodes* ticks that have fed on infected animals (Figure 2.27b).

Following a tick bite, the patient develops a red, circular lesion around the bite. This gradually enlarges, but the skin at the centre regains its normal appearance, so that the lesion resembles a ring (Figure 2.27c). Seven to ten days after the bite, a flu-like illness develops with headache, fever, chills and muscular aches. Ticks prefer to bite the armpits, scalp and groin, so the characteristic lesions may pass unnoticed and the illness be dismissed as a 'bit of flu'. However, weeks or months later, a secondary stage may develop causing inflammation of the heart, pericardium and joints. Antibodies produced by the host against *Borrelia* are thought to cross-react with the host's own molecules, resulting in the symptoms observed. Years later, a third stage to the disease may be seen, resembling Alzheimer's disease or multiple sclerosis, in that there is demyelination of neurons, resulting in behavioural changes. Comparisons have been made between *Borrelia burgdorferi* and *Treponema pallidum*, the bacterium responsible for syphilis. Both pathogens are spirochete bacteria and produce a disease with three distinct stages that may take years to develop.

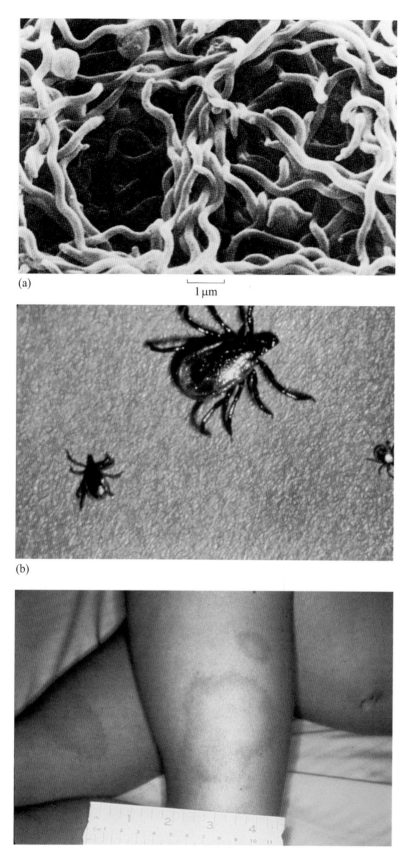

(a)

1 μm

(b)

(c)

FIGURE 2.27
Lyme disease. (a) Scanning electron micrograph of *Borrelia burgdorferi*. (b) The *Ixodes* tick, which spreads the disease. The tick on the right is an immature nymph; that on the left is an unengorged adult (about the size of a poppy seed) and the tick in the upper middle of the photo is an engorged adult (about the size of a jelly bean). (c) The typical rash with concentric rings around the site of the tick bite.

Summary of Section 2.7

1   Diseases that have appeared only recently include *E. coli* O157 and the zoonosis Lyme disease.

2   *E. coli* O157 produces several toxins, one of which kills vascular endothelial cells.

3   Lyme disease is transmitted by a tick bite and has three stages of increasing severity.

Learning outcomes for Chapter 2

When you have studied this chapter, you should be able to:

2.1   Define and use, or recognize definitions and applications of, each of the terms printed in **bold** in the text. (*all Section 2 questions*)

2.2   Show familiarity with a variety of styles of bacterial nomenclature used in microbiology. (*Questions 2.1 and 2.4*)

2.3   Explain the molecular organization that underlies different reactions to the Gram and Ziehl–Neelsen staining procedures. (*Questions 2.2 and 2.4*)

2.4   Demonstrate an understanding of the principle of selective toxicity. (*Questions 2.3 and 2.4*)

2.5   Using named examples, describe the relationship between commensals and pathogens. (*Question 2.5*)

2.6   Describe a range of named virulence factors and explain their modes of action. (*Questions 2.6 and 2.7*)

2.7   Describe the steps of the infection process. (*Question 2.8*)

2.8   Use named examples to describe different routes of infection by pathogenic bacteria. (*Question 2.9*)

2.9   Give examples and explain the aetiology of newly arising bacterial diseases. (*Question 2.10*)

Questions for Chapter 2

Question 2.1

Look at the list below and using the rules of nomenclature, write the plural forms of the genera shown. The first one is done for you.

Genus	Plural form
Bordetella	bordetellae
Borrelia	
Clostridium	
Corynebacterium	
Neisseria	
Salmonella	
Shigella	
Yersinia	

Question 2.2

Complete the table below, by adding information about the constituents of the bacterial surface.

Feature	Gram-positive	Gram-negative
peptidoglycan		
membranes		
teichoic acid		
lipid A		
lipopolysaccharide		

Question 2.3

Explain why an antibiotic that is active against bacteria, viruses and fungi is uncommon.

Question 2.4

Make a list of molecules found in acid-fast bacteria that might be used as targets for selective toxicity.

Question 2.5

Briefly explain how Doderlein's bacillus protects the female genital tract from infection, and how this mechanism could be affected by antibiotic treatment.

Question 2.6

Give one example of each class of microbial toxin, and explain briefly its mode of action.

Question 2.7

Explain what is meant by a virulence factor, and give an example of each group of virulence factors.

Question 2.8

What are the stages of the infection process?

Question 2.9

List the routes of infection used by the following pathogens: *Yersinia pestis, Staphylococcus aureus, Corynebacterium diphtheriae, Neisseria gonorrhoea, Salmonella typhi, Escherichia coli.*

Question 2.10

How can new infectious diseases appear?

3 THE VIRUSES

3.1 The history of the study of viruses

3.1.1 The filterable viruses

The late 19th century saw the discovery of many major pathogens, and a number of important diseases were being intensively studied then, in order to identify the pathogens or parasites that caused them.

▢ Recall the criteria used to identify the bacterial agent of a disease.

● Such agents must conform to Koch's postulates.

The invention of the porcelain bacterial filter in 1884 greatly aided the search, since liquids could be prepared that were known to be free of bacterial cells. In 1892 Dmitrii Iwanowsky, a Russian scientist, was working on a disease that affected the valuable tobacco crop. He found that leaf extracts from plants with the so-called tobacco mosaic disease, could cause this disease in healthy leaves, even after passage through a porcelain filter. In 1898 Martinus Beijerinck was also working on tobacco mosaic disease, while Friedrich Loeffler and Paul Frosch were studying foot-and-mouth disease in livestock. All of these researchers made the same observation, that a cell-free filtrate could still cause disease, and independently worked to characterize these mysterious disease-causing agents that were invisible under the light microscope.

▢ From reading Chapter 2, suggest a possible identity for the disease-causing substance.

● An obvious candidate is a bacterial toxin, which is a filterable molecule invisible under the light microscope.

However, the researchers established that the infective agent could proliferate inside infected cells, so it was unlikely to be a non-replicating molecule such as a toxin. Whatever the agent was, it needed living cells to reproduce. On the basis of this evidence it was suggested that a distinct, previously unrecognized type of pathogen was involved, and the term ultra-filterable virus was used to describe it. 'Virus' is a Latin word meaning venom or poison, and eventually these new infectious agents were simply called viruses. Despite this, no one actually saw a virus until 1941, a decade after the first electron microscope was built.

3.1.2 The discovery of bacteriophage

In 1915 Frederick Twort was trying to grow viruses on simple laboratory media. His cultures became contaminated with bacteria, but the colonies had an odd glassy appearance. Twort thought that a new kind of virus might have attacked the bacteria, but it was Félix d'Hérelle, in 1917, who actually demonstrated the existence of such a virus. He spread suspensions of this new type of virus onto agar plates previously spread with a bacterial culture. After incubation, the bacterial growth covered the plate but had numerous clear, circular areas in it where the bacteria had been lysed and killed. These cleared zones were termed viral **plaques**, and d'Herelle named the virus responsible for them **bacteriophage** (that is, something that eats bacteria – a bit of a misnomer, as you will see later). D'Hérelle believed that there was only one kind of bacteriophage, but later on many different kinds were discovered. Bacteriophages are among the best understood of the viruses, not least because they are so easily cultured. They have also been invaluable tools in the science of molecular biology (see Section 3.8).

3.1.3 The culture of viruses

Unlike bacteria or fungi, viruses cannot be cultured on artificial media, but require living cells. Early workers used natural hosts to grow viruses, but when human viruses were being studied, the risks to experimentally infected individuals quickly became unacceptable. Fertilized chicken eggs, containing a chick embryo, were found to be useful for the cultivation of viruses (see Figure 3.1). The eggs were inoculated using a fine needle and the needle hole was then plugged.

○ Why is it important to culture viruses?

● Viruses need to be cultured in order to study them and to prepare material for antiviral vaccines.

Virus culture in chicken eggs is still used for the preparation of some vaccines, e.g. against influenza, and this is the reason why some people with egg allergies need special preparations of such vaccines.

The development of **tissue culture** techniques, in the middle of the last century, made it possible to grow plant and animal cells *in vitro* (in the laboratory). The culture medium contains all the necessary nutrients for growth, and antimicrobial substances to help prevent the growth of bacteria and fungi. Contamination by these and other organisms is an important problem with tissue culture.

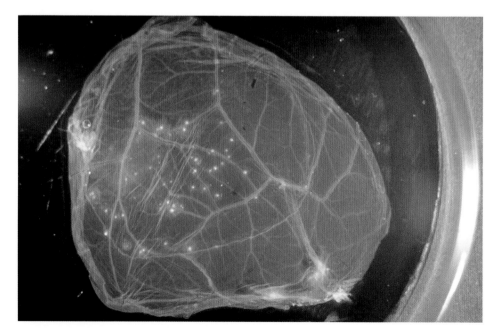

FIGURE 3.1
Viral plaques (the white spots) on an egg membrane.

Some viruses (e.g. hepatitis C virus, Section 3.7.3) cannot be grown in eggs or tissue culture, and whole animals are needed to cultivate these infectious agents. Whole animals are also used in viral pathogenesis studies, which investigate how a virus causes a particular disease. There are some viruses, such as Ebola (Section 3.7.1), that are so dangerous that cultivating them is a risky business and special precautions have to be taken. The study of all these agents should be made easier by the development of molecular biology techniques that allow manipulation of the viral genetic material rather than the infectious agent itself.

Summary of Section 3.1

1   Viruses were first discovered as filterable disease-causing substances that can replicate in host cells.

2   The first virus studied was tobacco mosaic virus.

3   The activity of bacterial viruses was first demonstrated in 1915, and they have been extensively studied since.

4   Viral culture techniques involve finding a suitable host that can be manipulated easily in the laboratory. This may be a whole organism or cells in tissue culture.

5   Some viruses can still not be cultured *in vitro*.

3.2 The nature of viruses

3.2.1 Are viruses alive?

Viruses are subcellular particles with no cytoplasm and no endogenous metabolic activity. This means that outside a host cell, viruses are almost entirely inactive collections of biological macromolecules. They are not produced by cycles of growth and division, but are assembled from preformed components, to give mature virus particles or **virions**. They are completely dependent on their host cell for the biosynthetic reactions needed for their replication. If by 'alive' we mean the ability to replicate, then viruses are alive, but life is usually viewed as far more than this. So-called computer viruses have the ability to replicate themselves, but we would never consider them to be alive!

Since viruses can replicate only inside host cells, they must move from one host to another to proliferate.

○   How has this knowledge informed the establishment of control measures against viruses? What has been the greatest success of this strategy?

●   Viruses need a population of susceptible individuals in order to persist. Vaccination programmes have been used to rob viruses of susceptible hosts, and have led to the eradication of some human viruses from many countries. For example, a worldwide vaccination programme against the smallpox virus during the 1970s eventually led to its extinction. At the time of writing (2002) there remain only a few reference stocks in laboratories, and there is an ongoing debate over whether or not to destroy them.

3.2.2 Virus structure

Viruses come in an astonishing variety of shapes (Figure 3.2) and sizes, ranging from 10–400 nm in diameter. All viruses have a nucleic acid genome, contained within a protein coat, the **capsid**. Viruses are subcellular infectious agents with a correspondingly small volume for their genetic material, which restricts the number of genes they carry. Some viruses also have a membrane or **envelope** surrounding their capsid, which is derived from the membranes of the previous host cell. The role of capsids and envelopes is to protect the viral genome from damage on its journey from one host cell to another. Damage may be caused by extremes of pH and temperature, uv light and the host immune response. The proteins that make up viral capsids are usually closely packed and highly folded, and this makes them difficult targets for any proteolytic enzymes that might attack them. The outer

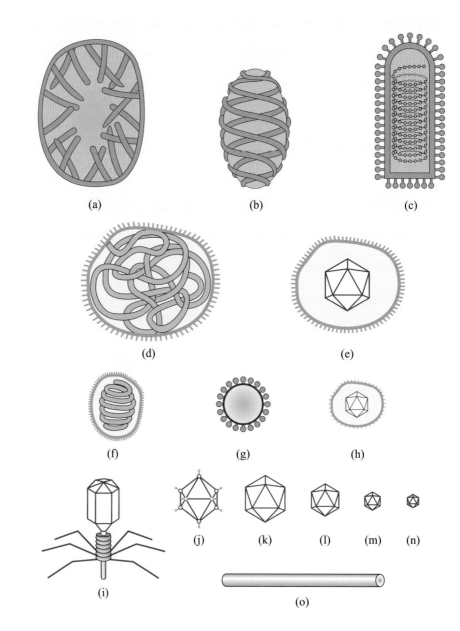

FIGURE 3.2
Morphology and approximate relative sizes of viruses.
(a) Orthopoxvirus.
(b) Parapoxvirus.
(c) Rhabdovirus.
(d) Paramyxovirus.
(e) Herpes virus.
(f) Orthomyxovirus.
(g) Coronavirus;
(h) Togavirus.
(i) T-even bacteriophage.
(j) Adenovirus.
(k) Reovirus.
(l) Papovavirus.
(m) Picornavirus.
(n) Parvovirus.
(o) Tobacco mosaic virus.
Note: although (j)–(n) are all icosahedral viruses, their sizes (and of course their coat proteins) are characteristic of the different virus groups. The same applies to (e) and (h), which are both enveloped icosahedrons, but are different sizes and have different coat and envelope molecules.

structure of a virus particle also mediates attachment to new host cells, and the molecules involved present targets for the host immune response.

Capsids are made up of multiple copies of smaller protein units called **protomers** or structural units. A protomer may be constructed from just one protein, or several different protein subunits. Some viruses, for example tobacco mosaic virus (TMV), which causes the tobacco mosaic disease studied by the earliest virologists, have only one type of protomer comprising one protein, so a single gene encodes the entire protein coat. Other viruses have more than one type of protomer and each protomer may have several different subunits, but the total number of different kinds of protein remains small, so that only a small part of the genome codes for the capsid. The proteins of the capsid are arranged so that they make the maximum amount of contact with one another, and are held together by non-covalent bonds. Such interactions between a limited number of proteins give rise to a regular and symmetrical capsid, usually in the shape of either a **helix** or an **icosahedron**; for example, TMV has a helical capsid. Each one of its identical protomers is folded to give a clog-like shape, and these join together to give a 'spiral staircase', where each structural unit represents a step (see Figure 3.3). The viral genome lies in a groove on the inside of each protomer as shown, and this association of protein and nucleic acid is so intimate the whole structure is described as a **nucleocapsid.**

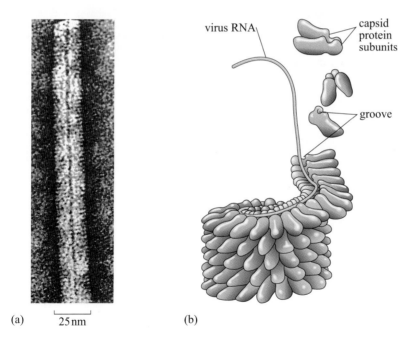

(a)   25 nm   (b)

FIGURE 3.3
The nucleocapsid of TMV. (a) Electron micrograph of part of a TMV particle. (b) Assembly of a TMV virion. The viral nucleic acid (RNA) is arranged helically around a hollow core, and is held in this configuration by the assembly of identical capsid protein subunits, forming the nucleocapsid.

Icosahedral capsids are roughly spherical in shape, and made up of 20 identical flat surfaces, each one forming an equilateral triangle, as shown in Figure 3.4 overleaf. Although the volume enclosed varies depending on the size of the proteins, this simple icosahedron is still rather small and can only accommodate small genomes. The simplest icosahedral capsid has three identical protein molecules making up each of the 20 faces, giving a total of 60 protomers overall. The canine parvovirus is like this. However, most icosahedral capsids are more complicated, such as the polio virus capsid (polio virus causes the disease poliomyelitis), which is also made up of 60 protomers, but with each protomer composed of *four* different protein subunits, making a total of 240 subunits overall (see Figure 3.5). Even more complicated are the adenoviruses, which cause respiratory disease, conjunctivitis and gut infections. These icosahedral viruses have 780 subunits making up their capsids, which also have special fibres projecting from their vertices or 'corners' (see Figure 3.6).

◯ Which axis of symmetry is shown in Figure 3.6b?

⬤ The twofold axis (compare Figure 3.4c).

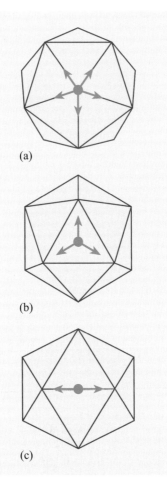

FIGURE 3.4 An icosahedron viewed along its (a) fivefold; (b) threefold; (c) twofold axes of symmetry. To understand the term 'axis of symmetry', imagine folding an object in such a way that the two halves either side of the line of the fold can be exactly superimposed. The imaginary line is an axis of symmetry.

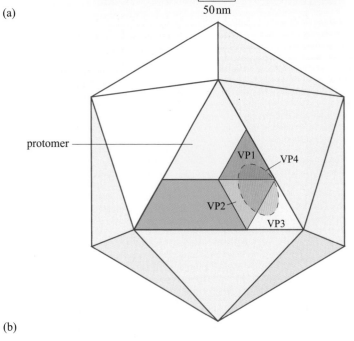

(a)

50 nm

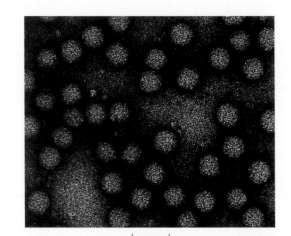

protomer

VP1
VP4
VP2
VP3

(b)

FIGURE 3.5 Polio virus. (a) Electron micrograph of polio viruses. (b) Diagram of the polioviral virion, showing the subunit composition of one of the three protomers that make up each capsid face. VP = viral protein. Note that VP4 lies beneath the other three, on the inside of the capsid.

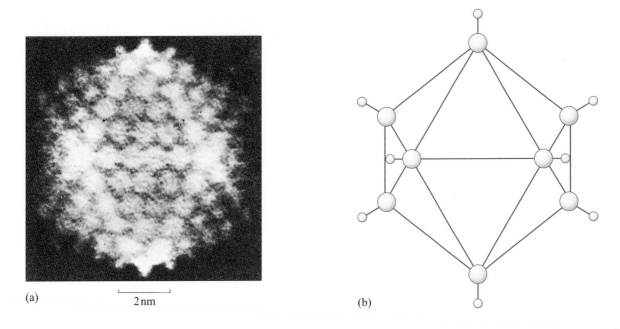

(a) 2 nm (b)

FIGURE 3.6 Adenovirus. (a) Electron micrograph of adenovirus. (b) Diagram of the edges of the icosahedron, and the spikes at the vertices of the virion.

Some viral capsids have a **complex** structure and are neither simply helical nor icosahedral. T (tailed) bacteriophages, which attack *E. coli*, have an icosahedral head attached to a helical tail, and some even have tail fibres attached to their base-plate (Figure 3.7). They have been described as lunar landing modules, and it is not difficult to see why. Other viruses with a complex architecture are the poxviruses, the family that includes the smallpox virus. These viruses have a membrane-bound structure called a nucleosome containing their genome, which is enclosed within other membranes and an exterior coat covered in fibres (see Figure 3.8 overleaf).

Most helical and many icosahedral viruses are enveloped with a membrane that is derived from their host cell. The membrane may be loose fitting around the capsid or core, obscuring its shape (as is the case with influenza virus; see below), or drawn closely around the protein coat to give a characteristic appearance. Although viral envelopes are derived from the host, they contain virus-encoded glycoproteins, usually of just one or two kinds. The viral glycoproteins are anchored in the membrane, but project above it to the outside and below it to the virion interior. The exterior domains of these proteins are major antigens, and are involved in virus interactions with host cells, while the interior domains can be important in virus assembly. In addition, larger viruses sometimes have protein layers between their capsids and envelopes, which maintain connections between the layers. The simplest of these is the M or matrix protein that lies just beneath the envelope in, for example, the influenza virus and the measles virus (see Figures 3.10 and 3.12 on pp. 72 and 73). This protein is bound to both the capsid and the envelope and holds them together.

Having considered the outer protective layers of the virion, we will now take a look inside. As mentioned before, viral genomes are small, ranging from a few thousand to 250 000 nucleotides. Viral genomes are amazingly diverse: they may be single or double-stranded, linear or circular, or even split into separate molecules called

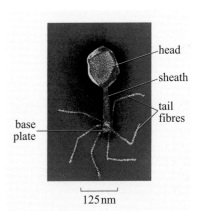

head
sheath
tail fibres
base plate
125 nm

FIGURE 3.7
A false-colour electron micrograph of a T-even phage which infects *E. coli*.

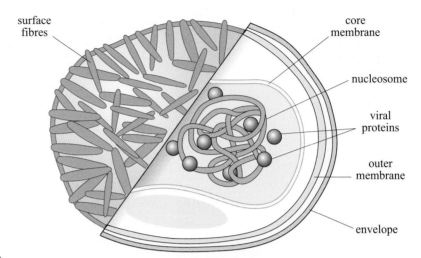

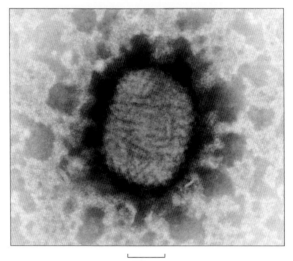

(a)

(b)

60 nm

FIGURE 3.8
Poxviruses. (a) Vaccinia virus: the left side shows the structure of the unenveloped virion and the right side shows a section of the enveloped virion. (b) Electron micrograph of molluscum contagiosum virus.

segments. One plant virus with a segmented genome, the brome mosaic virus, even has each segment packaged separately in its own virion! Infection requires all three virions to inject their contents into the same cell.

 From this information, what would you predict about the infectivity of brome mosaic virus?

It would not be transferred from one plant to the next with very high efficiency, so would not be very infectious.

Eukaryotic and prokaryotic cells contain both DNA and RNA, but individual viral capsids only ever contain either RNA or DNA, never both. Viruses that have RNA as their genetic material are known as **RNA viruses**. Most RNA viruses have single-stranded RNA. If the genomic viral RNA is equivalent to mRNA, i.e. it contains immediately translatable information, it is described as a positive, plus (+) or sense strand. Most single-stranded RNA viruses, such as polio virus, have positive strand genomes. However if the genomic viral RNA cannot be immediately translated, because it is *complementary* to mRNA, it is referred to as a negative, minus (−) or antisense strand. All negative strand RNA viruses have helical capsids, and many of them have segmented genomes. Influenza A, the virus that causes the most serious type of influenza, has a negative strand RNA genome split into eight segments (Book 1, Chapter 2 case study). Some single-stranded RNA viruses have **ambisense RNA**, which has both positive and negative RNA present on the same strand. Finally, there are double-stranded RNA viruses, which all have segmented genomes.

The viruses that have DNA genomes are called **DNA viruses**, an example of which is the virus that caused smallpox, and most of them contain double-stranded DNA. All the human DNA viruses, apart from poxviruses, synthesize their mRNA and DNA in the nucleus of the host cell where the appropriate host enzymes, such as RNA polymerase, are located. In contrast, poxviruses synthesize their mRNA and DNA entirely in the cytoplasm (see below).

- ◯ What is the obvious drawback to this strategy?

- ⬤ The host enzymes involved in DNA and RNA synthesis are unavailable in the cytoplasm, so a different approach must be used for viral replication.

Viral proteins may be split into three types: the structural proteins, which form the virion; the non-structural proteins, which are present in infected cells; and a third type, which is neither exactly structural nor non-structural. For example, many viruses carry their own enzymes in their capsids, so these enzymes are therefore a part of the virion structure, but they are also present in an infected cell. Viruses sometimes carry their own enzymes because the host does not possess the required enzyme, or it is inaccessible. For example, negative strand RNA viruses require an RNA-dependent RNA polymerase to produce their own mRNA for translation. This reaction is never required in the host, since mRNA is always produced from a DNA template. The poxviruses carry their own DNA-dependent RNA polymerase because transcription of the DNA genome takes place in the cytoplasm, and the equivalent enzyme in the host is found only in the nucleus, as remarked above.

3.2.3 The origin of viruses

Viruses leave no fossil record to help us determine when they first emerged and where they might fit onto an evolutionary tree. They are simpler than bacteria, but cannot propagate themselves without a host cell, so their origins are somewhat mysterious. There are several theories that attempt to explain how the viruses arose. **Retrograde evolution** theories suggest they may have evolved from other intracellular parasites, most likely prokaryotic cells, by shedding all but the most essential genes. Species persist only as long as they can pass their genes on to a new generation, and in this sense, viruses could be highly evolved parasites that perform only this function. However, since viruses and prokaryotic cells are so different, it is difficult to see how such a process could have taken place.

A second theory puts forward the idea that viruses evolved from cellular components that are composed of nucleic acid, such as plasmids and transposons. Plasmids and transposons can replicate themselves independently of the cell genome, and some plasmids are able to transfer themselves from one cell to another. If such a plasmid acquired genes coding for a protein coat, it would have the makings of a virus. Viroids, which are the causative agents of some plant diseases, might represent a step in this process. These small, circular RNA molecules are infectious, but do not code for any protein. They pass from cell to cell only when the membranes of both cells are damaged.

Finally, there is a theory suggesting that viruses have existed since the origin of life and have coevolved with cells. Viruses are so diverse, that it may be wrong to assume they share a common origin. It could be that all three theories are correct!

Summary of Section 3.2

1   Whether viruses are 'alive' remains a controversial point.

2   Viruses are completely dependent on their host cells for proliferation.

3   Viruses consist of a nucleic acid genome contained within a capsid. Some viruses have an additional envelope, derived from host cell membranes.

4   Capsids are generally helical or icosahedral, though others may have a more complex structure.

5   Viral nucleic acid may be DNA or RNA, single- or double-stranded, and may be present as one or more distinct molecules; RNA genomes may be in sense (+), antisense (−) or ambisense strands.

6   The evolutionary origin of viruses is obscure.

3.3 Different types of virus

3.3.1 Classification of viruses

Viruses can be classified in several ways. First, they can be classified according to the type of host they infect, as animal, plant or bacterial (bacteriophage) viruses. They can then be distinguished by their genetic content, the size and shape of their capsids, and whether they are enveloped or 'naked'. Using these criteria, animal viruses are sorted into families, genera and individual types, although in contrast to the more familiar biological groups, these terms have no evolutionary meaning. The families have both English and Latin names. An English name may be changed into a Latin one by substituting the ending '-viruses' with '-viridae'; e.g. Poxviruses becomes Poxviridae. Such a classification system cannot show the evolutionary relationships of the various viruses, since this is largely unknown (although nucleotide sequencing methods are now shedding light on this subject), but they do enable us to make sense of this group of pathogens.

In 1971, the US microbiologist David Baltimore proposed an additional classification system based on the character of the viral genome. All viruses have to direct the synthesis of mRNA in order to have their proteins made by the host cell. As you have seen, viral genomes vary widely, and different viruses have different ways of producing the necessary mRNA. Baltimore proposed that viruses be classified depending on the steps they took to produce mRNA that could be translated by the host cell. Subsequently other groups of virus were discovered, and the original Baltimore classification was extended. The seven Baltimore classes are shown in Figure 3.9. Baltimore's system complemented the existing classification system, and highlighted the central importance of mRNA in viral replication. The classification of selected human pathogens, using both classification systems, is illustrated in Table 3.1.

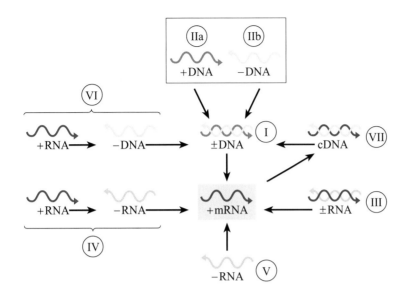

FIGURE 3.9
The updated Baltimore classification of viruses. The classification is based on the steps viruses take to produce mRNA.

TABLE 3.1 Classification of selected viruses that are human pathogens.

Virus	Disease caused	Genus	Family	Genome	Baltimore group	Capsid	Envelope
influenza	flu	no separate genera, just influenza A, B and C	Orthomyxoviridae	RNA, ss (−)	V	helical	yes
HIV	AIDS	no genera; HIV belongs to Lentiviridae subfamily	Retroviridae	RNA, ss (+)	VI	icosahedral	yes
polio	polio	Enterovirus	Picornaviridae	RNA, ss (+)	IV	icosahedral	no
variola	smallpox	Orthopoxvirus	Poxviridae	DNA, ds	I	complex	yes
measles	measles	Morbillivirus	Paramyxoviridae	RNA, ss (−)	V	helical	yes
hepatitis B virus	hepatitis	no genera	Hepadnaviridae	DNA, partially ds	VII	complex	yes
reovirus	mild respiratory and gastric disease	Orthoreovirus	Reoviridae	RNA, ds, segmented	III	icosahedral	no
B19	erythema infectiosum (fifth disease*)	Parvovirus	Parvoviridae	DNA, ss (+ and − in different virions)	II	icosahedral	no

* So named because, in the pre-vaccination era, it was frequently the fifth disease that a child would develop.

During this course, several viruses and the diseases they cause will be studied in greater depth as case studies. You have already met influenza (Figure 3.10); the other case study viruses, in order of appearance, are HIV (Figure 3.11) and polio (Figure 3.5 above), and some aspects of infection with the smallpox (Figure 3.8 above) and measles (Figure 3.12) viruses will also be looked at in detail.

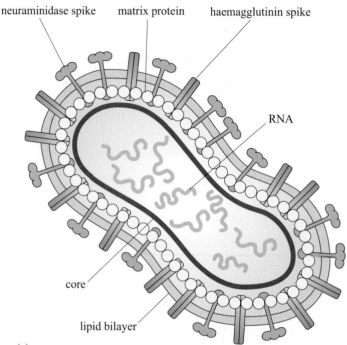

(a)

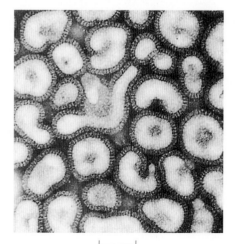

(b)

500 nm

FIGURE 3.10
Structure of the influenza virus.
(a) Diagram of the virion. (b) Electron micrograph of human influenza virus particles. Note that the basic helical shape is obscured by the loose envelope.

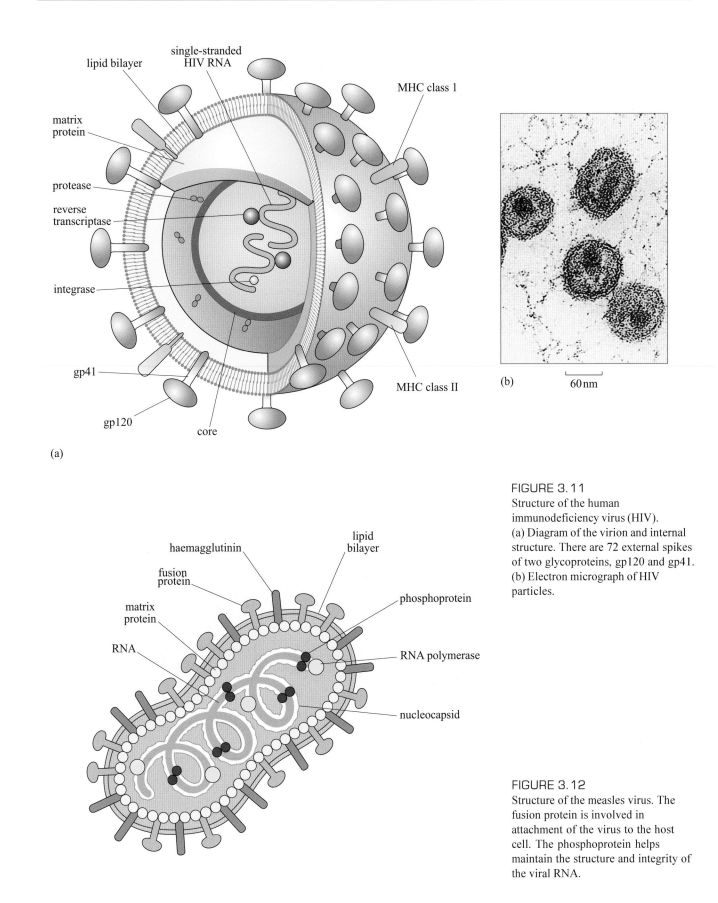

(a)

(b)   60 nm

FIGURE 3.11
Structure of the human immunodeficiency virus (HIV).
(a) Diagram of the virion and internal structure. There are 72 external spikes of two glycoproteins, gp120 and gp41.
(b) Electron micrograph of HIV particles.

FIGURE 3.12
Structure of the measles virus. The fusion protein is involved in attachment of the virus to the host cell. The phosphoprotein helps maintain the structure and integrity of the viral RNA.

73

3.3.2 Retroviruses and the central dogma of gene expression

In order for a protein to be made, the DNA encoding it has first to be transcribed into mRNA, and then this mRNA is translated to give the protein product. This flow of information from DNA to RNA to protein is known as the **central dogma of gene expression**. In 1970 this one-way flow of information was challenged by the discovery of an enzyme that could produce DNA from an RNA template. This RNA-dependent DNA polymerase was called **reverse transcriptase**, and it occurs in a group of viruses known as retroviruses (group VI in the Baltimore classification). HIV, the virus that causes AIDS is a retrovirus, and you will learn more about it as you study this course (HIV/AIDS Case Study). Another group of viruses is now known to produce reverse transcriptase; these are the DNA reverse-transcribing viruses (group VII in the Baltimore classification).

Summary of Section 3.3

1   Viruses can be classified in several ways, such as by shape or size, host, type of capsid, family and genus, replication strategy, or nucleotide sequence.

2   Reverse-transcribing viruses make DNA from an RNA template and hence challenge the central dogma of gene expression.

3.4 Viral replication strategies

How a virus finds and infects a cell, replicates itself and releases its progeny from the host cell is called its replication strategy. The main points of this process are summarized below, but if you are new to virology or want a reminder, a detailed description can be found on the Reference CD: S204 Book 4, Chapter 1.

3.4.1 Generalized replication strategy

A virus must first enter a suitable host and come into contact with a cell it can infect. Such cells have molecules on their surface that bind specifically to corresponding receptors on the viral surface. The virus is said to be **tropic** (meaning 'prefers') for the cells it can infect, and this tropism includes the *species* that can be infected as well as the particular *cell types*. The human immunodeficiency virus (type 1) binds a molecule on human cell surfaces known as CD4.

☐   What would you predict from this information about the tissue tropism of HIV?

◓   It would follow the tissue distribution of CD4.

Indeed, the distribution of CD4 mirrors almost exactly the tissue tropism of HIV. However, the relationship between a virus and its specific ligand is not always so straightforward; for example, the polio virus can replicate only in *some* of the cell types that possess the polio virus receptor (Pvr).

☐   What does this suggest about viral tropism?

◓   It is affected by factors other than initial host–virus binding.

Studies have found that some sequences of viral genomes known as **enhancers**, which are involved in controlling viral transcription, are only functional in certain cell types: the hepatitis B virus enhancer, for example, is only active in liver cells.

Once attached, the virus is taken up into the host cell and can **uncoat**, that is, release the viral nucleic acid. This marks the end of the **initiation phase,** and is followed by the replication of the viral genome and expression of the viral proteins. The first genes to be expressed are known as **early genes**, while the remaining genes, which include those encoding the capsid proteins, are termed **late genes**. When gene expression is complete, new virions may be **assembled** from their components. Many viruses require yet another stage, called **maturation**, before they are capable of infecting a new host cell. The details of maturation vary between viruses, but often the process involves structural changes mediated by viral proteases. These proteases can be used as therapeutic targets, as in the case of HIV, because they differ quite extensively from host proteases.

◯ What is the principle exploited in this therapeutic strategy?

⬤ The principle of selective toxicity (Section 2.2.1).

The mature virions are then released from the host cell, either by lysing the cell or budding from the membrane of the intact cell.

3.4.2 Replication strategies of some important viruses

Influenza virus and HIV

The replication strategies for these viruses can be found in the appropriate case studies (influenza is in Book 1, Chapter 2).

Polio virus

The polio virus belongs to the family of Picornaviridae, so-called because they are small (pico) RNA viruses. Their single-stranded genomes are made of positive RNA. The polio virus belongs to a subgroup (genus) of Picornaviridae known as enteroviruses, which, as the name suggests, affect the gut. Enteroviruses are some of the most stable viruses known and can persist for weeks at room temperature. They are also stable in acidic conditions down to pH 3, and this enables them to pass through the stomach and infect their host via the intestinal tract. Sometimes the virus spreads to the bloodstream, and occasionally it reaches the central nervous system. Children are the most likely hosts of these viruses, and in temperate latitudes most infections occur in the spring and autumn.

Picornaviruses have naked icosahedral capsids 27–30 nm in diameter, made up of 60 protomers. Each protomer is constructed from four different viral proteins (VPs) called VP1, VP2, VP3 and VP4 (see Figure 3.5b). The replication cycle of polio viruses begins when a virion binds a specific receptor on the surface of a host cell that it is able to infect, as shown in Figure 3.13a overleaf. The receptors are host cell membrane glycoproteins, which interact with the viral capsid so that it becomes attached to the membrane. After attachment, VP4 is lost from the capsid, causing its structure to change dramatically. Penetration into the host cell and uncoating of the viral genome then follow, but the precise mechanisms involved are not fully understood.

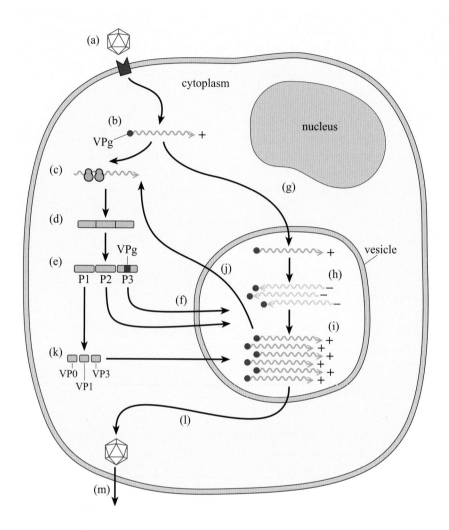

FIGURE 3.13 The replicative cycle of polio virus. (a) The virion binds a host receptor. (b) The (+) RNA genome is uncoated. (c) The mRNA is translated to a single polyprotein (d), which is cleaved into three separate polyproteins, P1, P2 and P3 (e). P2 and P3 enter a membrane-bound vesicle (f). Meanwhile, the original (+) strand also passes into the vesicle (g) where it is copied into several (−) strands (h). The (−) strands are copied to many (+) strands (i), some of which may be used as translation templates (j). The remainder assemble with the cleavage products of P1 (k), and new virions come out of the vesicle (l) and leave the host cell (m).

Once initiation of infection is complete, the replication phase begins. The viral genome forms one giant (for a virus!) mRNA molecule 6000 nucleotides long, which encodes a number of different genes, and which has another viral protein, VPg, attached at its 5′ end. The VPg protein is removed prior to translation of the mRNA. The translation product is a large polyprotein that is cleaved into three separate polyproteins known as P1, P2 and P3. The polyprotein P1 contains the capsid proteins, while P2 and P3 contain the proteases and other proteins, including VPg, which are needed for viral RNA synthesis (see Figure 3.14). The viral RNA is first copied into one or more complementary negative strands with VPg attached at the 3′ end. This then serves as a template for the synthesis of new positive strand RNA viral genomes with VPg at their 5′ ends. RNA synthesis takes place on the surface of special membrane-bound vesicles associated with the smooth

5′ and 3′ are the two ends of a DNA or RNA molecule.

endoplasmic reticulum. Some of the newly synthesized strands have VPg removed and are translated to provide more viral proteins. The capsid proteins, VPO, VP1 and VP3, assemble with viral genomes to form virus particles. Maturation then takes place with the cleavage of VPO to give VP2 and VP4 (not shown in Figure 3.13). A host cell infected with polio virus is unable to synthesize its own mRNA or proteins, and 5–10 hours after infection it dies. The death and lysis of the host cell releases the progeny virions, which may then infect further cells. You will learn about the application of this knowledge later in the course (see Polio Case Study).

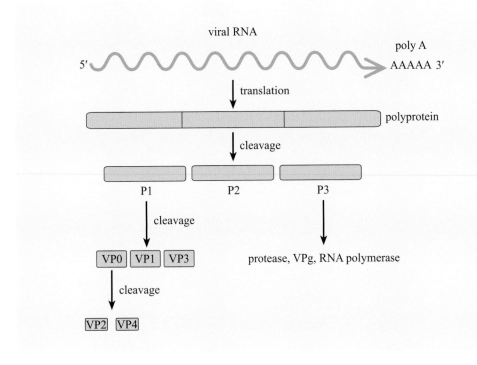

FIGURE 3.14
The synthesis of polyproteins in poliovirus. Poly A is a string of adenine nucleotides at the 3′ end.

Smallpox virus

Poxviruses are the largest animal viruses and can even be seen with a light microscope under certain conditions. Most poxviruses that infect humans cause only minor skin lesions, but smallpox virus caused one of the most deadly viral infections in human history. The family Poxviridae is divided into six genera, with the smallpox and vaccinia viruses making up the Orthopoxvirus genus. The smallpox virus has been effectively extinct since 1977, but the details of its replication strategy are still of interest.

Poxviruses have a complex architecture, with no obvious symmetry and a nucleosome containing their double-stranded DNA genomes (see Figure 3.8a above). Unusually, the two DNA strands are covalently linked together at both ends, giving one large, circular DNA molecule. Poxviruses, unlike other DNA viruses, replicate entirely in the cytoplasm and must supply their own enzymes for nucleic acid synthesis. These enzymes, including a DNA-dependent RNA polymerase, are found in the nucleosome and make up a transcriptional system for producing their mRNA. However, they still use host precursors and energy supplies.

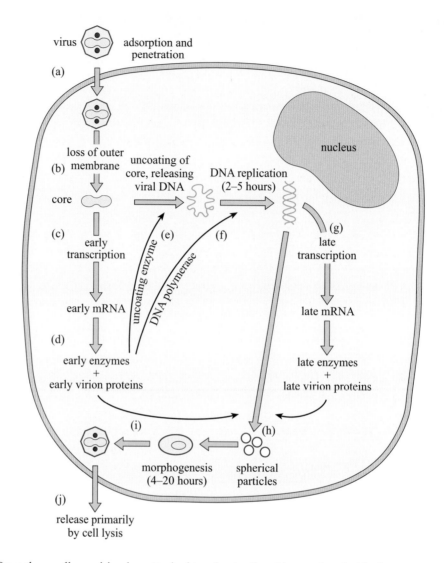

FIGURE 3.15

Replication of smallpox virus. (a) The virus attaches to the cell and is internalized. (b) A core is released, which undergoes transcription of early genes (c). The transcripts are used to make early proteins (d), one of which uncoats the core to release the viral DNA (e). The DNA is replicated by an 'early' viral DNA polymerase (f), and the late genes are then transcribed (g) and translated. Both early and late proteins contribute to the capsid (h), but structural rearrangements are needed to make the mature virions (i), which are released by cell lysis (j).

Once the smallpox virion has attached to a host cell and been taken inside, it uncoats and starts to synthesize its mRNA (see Figure 3.15). A number of early genes, which together make up around half of the genome, are transcribed and translated straight away.

☐ Suggest possible roles for the early proteins.

⬤ They could be enzymes that allow the viral DNA to be replicated and transcribed, or for uncoating the core.

Using such enzymes, DNA replication begins around 90 minutes after a cell has been infected, and this process brings about a change in viral gene expression. The late genes start to be transcribed while the early genes are switched off. Late genes encode most of the proteins required to build the virus particles. Virion assembly involves a number of different steps and, like replication and transcription, occurs in the cytoplasm. The majority of the mature virions are released from the host cell when it dies and lyses, but a few mature virions can acquire an envelope from structures in the host cell, allowing them to leave the cell while it is still intact. As soon as the smallpox virus begins to make its own proteins, host cell protein synthesis is irreversibly inhibited.

Measles virus

The measles virus belongs to the family Paramyxoviridae, which also includes the virus that causes mumps. Measles and mumps both cause systemic disease, but other members of the family, such as parainfluenza viruses, cause acute respiratory infections. The paramyxoviruses resemble the orthomyxoviruses such as influenza in their structure, and share with them an ability to bind receptors containing the sugar sialic acid, but paramyxoviruses are larger in size. Like the orthomyxoviruses they have helical, enveloped capsids enclosing a negative strand RNA genome, but in contrast to the orthomyxoviruses their genomes are not segmented. The replication strategy of the measles virus is similar to that of the influenza virus (see Influenza Case Study) and is described below.

After attaching to a host cell and uncoating, the RNA genome is ready to be copied into a positive RNA strand, which can serve as mRNA (Figure 3.16). This mRNA is translated to yield viral proteins, and the negative genome is copied into a positive replicative intermediate. The replicative intermediate is then used as a template to produce many copies of the negative strand viral genome, and the replicative intermediate may also enter the translation system so that more viral proteins can be

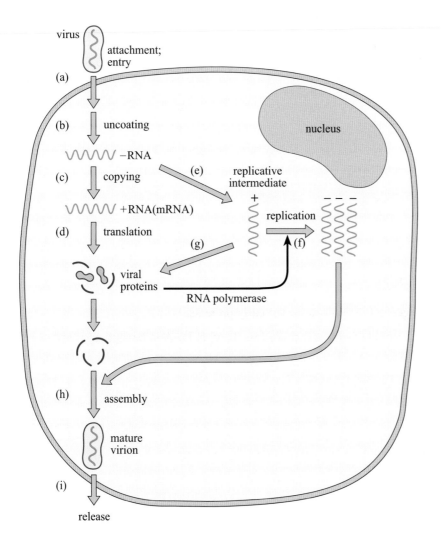

FIGURE 3.16
Replication of measles virus. (a) The virus attaches to and penetrates the host cell. (b) The (−) RNA is uncoated and (c) copied to a (+) strand, which is translated to give viral proteins (d). The (−) strand is also copied (e) to give a (+) replicative intermediate, which is used to make many (−) copies of the genome (f), and may also be translated (g). The translation products include enzymes for replication, and capsid proteins. The genomes and capsid proteins assemble (h), and mature virions are released from the host cell (i).

synthesized. Unlike influenza virus, which is partly assembled in the nucleus, the measles virus is entirely replicated in the cytoplasm. The number of nucleocapsids assembled in the cytoplasm is so large that they are visible as inclusion bodies (see Section 3.5). Finally, the mature virions are released from the host cell by budding.

Summary of Section 3.4

1   Generally, replicating viruses undergo attachment, uncoating, genome replication, expression of early and late genes, maturation and release.

2   There are seven distinct replication strategies and the details of these processes are highly variable.

3.5 Effects of viral infection on the host's cells

A variety of possible fates await a cell infected with a virus, and they fall into several categories. Animal experiments have shown that some viruses produce no discernible pathological damage to the host's cells. Not surprisingly, such infections are also asymptomatic. In direct contrast, some viruses, such as picornaviruses, described as **cytocidal**, quickly kill their host cell, releasing many progeny in the process. **Non-cytocidal** viruses replicate and release their progeny without killing the host cell immediately, like influenza. Cytocidal and non-cytocidal viruses both cause acute infections in their hosts. Sometimes a virus will infect a cell, produce few or no progeny, and the host cell remains largely intact. This type of viral infection is described as **persistent**. The HIV virus establishes a persistent infection.

Generally, viruses may produce a number of deleterious effects on the host cell. Any deleterious changes in host cells or tissues caused by a viral infection are described as **cytopathic** effects. In cultured cells infected with virus, these changes may be apparent with a light microscope. For example, cultured cells may appear rounded up, or their nuclei may be swollen, and some cells may even fuse to form giant cells called **syncytia**.

○   Suggest what is happening in the infected cells.

●   Their own metabolism is corrupted, and they can often synthesize no protein of their own at all.

Pathogenic viruses, especially cytocidal ones, produce factors that inhibit the synthesis of host DNA, RNA and protein. Polio virus, for example, produces proteins known as 2A and 3C that inhibit host cell translation and transcription respectively. Despite this, it isn't entirely clear how these viruses kill their host cell, since the cells actually die before they have exhausted their protein supplies. It may be that the integrity of the plasma membrane is compromised.

○   Why might damage to the plasma membrane lead to the death of the host cell?

●   The different concentrations of Na^+ ions and K^+ ions inside and outside the cell may no longer be maintained, and dissipation of these ion gradients can have disastrous consequences, such as osmotic lysis (bursting).

Cells infected with a virus are often found to have viral proteins in their plasma membranes (see Book 3).

○ What effect would the presence of viral proteins in host plasma membranes have on the immune system?

● The immune system would recognize viral proteins as foreign antigens, and would mount an appropriate response.

Alterations to the membranes of a group of infected cells can lead to the membranes fusing to form a giant, multinucleate cell (like the syncytia observed in culture). Such cells are seen in measles and HIV infections, where as many as 50 or 100 cells can fuse together. Viruses may also damage intracellular membranes, such as those of lysosomes, allowing the degradative enzymes to leak out, leading to self-digestion and resulting lysis.

Another morphological change seen in virally infected cells is the appearance of granular **inclusion bodies**. In this context, the granules of the inclusion bodies consist of sites where new viral components are being synthesized. These sites may be found in organelles, the cytosol or the nucleus, depending on the virus involved, and can damage the cell's ultrastructure. Poxviruses form inclusion bodies in the cytoplasm, whereas the measles virus forms them in both the cytoplasm and the nucleus. Adenoviruses (DNA viruses that cause respiratory disease, conjunctivitis and gut infections) are assembled in the nucleus. The newly synthesized viral components often pack together to form a crystal-like structure known as a paracrystalline array, shown in Figure 3.17. Viruses that penetrate the cell nucleus, such as adenoviruses and herpes viruses (DNA viruses that cause cold sores and genital herpes), may also disrupt the chromosomes and cause further damage to an infected cell.

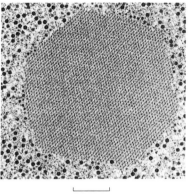

1 μm

FIGURE 3.17
Paracrystalline array of adenovirus inside a host cell nucleus.

Viral replication requires a functioning cell, so it is in the interest of the virus not to kill the host cell until the progeny have been produced. Conversely, it is in the host's interest that the virally infected cell should die as soon as possible. Apoptosis (programmed cell death) is therefore an important mechanism of host defence, and is demonstrated by cells infected with viruses such as HIV, influenza and picornaviruses. Of course, viruses have evolved their own counterstrategies; some synthesize proteins that inhibit apoptosis while others have gene products that delay it until the process is convenient for them – apoptosis may release the progeny virions.

Some viral proteins may be toxic to the host, either because they accumulate in high concentrations during replication or because individual proteins may have deleterious effects. An example of this is the gp120 viral envelope protein of HIV, which triggers apoptosis in neurons by altering the intracellular concentration of calcium ions. The consequent loss of neurons is thought to be the cause of AIDS-associated dementia.

Summary of Section 3.5

1 Pathogenic viruses may be cytocidal, and kill the host cell quickly, or non-cytocidal, in which case persistent infections may ensue.

2 Viruses often have cytopathic effects such as the formation of syncytia and inclusion bodies, membrane damage, or the triggering of apoptosis.

3.6 Effect of viral infection on the host's body

Many viruses cause acute infections, where there is a rapid onset of symptoms followed by recovery, and a complete elimination of the virus from the body. Other viruses can cause persistent infections, where the virus remains in the host for an extended period. They halt any cytopathic activity and successfully evade the host immune system. Some viruses can adopt both strategies: Varicella zoster, the herpesvirus that causes chickenpox, also causes a type of persistent infection described as latent. Following the acute chickenpox infection, the virus persists in the sensory nerves without replicating and is undetectable or hidden, hence the term 'latent'. Years later, the virus can reactivate, on more than one occasion, to produce the skin disease shingles.

Another type of persistent infection is called a **slow infection**, because following an initial acute stage, the virus persists and eventually brings about symptoms that kill the host. An example of a slow viral infection is subacute sclerosing panencephalitis, which occasionally may be caused by the measles virus (see Section 3.6.1).

Some infections with DNA viruses or retroviruses can damage a cell by **transforming** it, that is, changing its behaviour. Transformation is sometimes associated with integration of viral nucleic acid into the host genome, disrupting the normal genetic sequence. The transformed cell lacks the regulatory mechanisms found in a healthy cell and may grow faster than its neighbours. Such transformed cells can cause cancer, and several human cancers have been linked with viruses. For example, some types of cervical cancer are associated with certain papilloma viruses (Section 8.2).

3.6.1 Examples of the effects of viral infection on the host

Details of the effects of influenza, HIV and polio infections on the host are addressed in the relevant case study.

The effect of a smallpox virus infection on the host

Smallpox was among the deadliest viruses in history, and as it was spread by the respiratory route, it was very contagious. Smallpox could also persist in the environment and on contaminated fomites (inanimate objects) for a very long time. The virus established an infection by targeting epithelial cells in the upper respiratory tract. Then it spread to local lymph nodes, and from there to the blood (viraemia). This primary viraemia was relatively light, but allowed the virus to infect cells throughout the body, resulting in a more intense secondary viraemia. It was at this point that symptoms appeared, starting with a fever. The virus multiplied in the skin cells which eventually produced the typical rash of vesicles (small blisters) and pustules (pus-filled pimples) (Figure 3.18). These lesions left permanent scars, particularly on the face. In recent times, just two types of smallpox were recognized: variola major virus and variola minor virus. Variola major caused the characteristic smallpox disease, with a case fatality rate ranging from 10–50%, whereas variola minor infections were much less severe, with a case fatality rate of less than 1%. These two smallpox viruses were very similar, but could be distinguished from one another by differences in their genomes.

FIGURE 3.18
A person with smallpox.

The effect of a measles virus infection on the host

Measles is an acute contagious disease spread by droplet infection, and is endemic the world over. It is estimated that in developing countries where nutrition is poor, measles kills more children than smallpox ever did. In a measles infection, there is typically a 10-day incubation period, during which the virus replicates and spreads, before the symptoms actually appear. The virus enters the body via the respiratory tract or the conjunctiva, and spreads through the lymph nodes to the blood, causing viraemia. The virus is able to replicate in a variety of sites, including the cells of the nervous and immune systems. The release of progeny virus into the blood from these additional sites causes a secondary viraemia, which involves more virus particles than the first viraemic episode. Following this second viraemia, symptoms begin with a cough, runny nose, fever and conjunctivitis. Bright red spots with a bluish-white centre, known as Koplik's spots, may also appear in the mouth. This is followed by a rash, made up of macules (spots discolouring the skin) and papules (solid pimples), which lasts for 5–10 days (see Figure 3.19). There is no specific treatment for measles, but fortunately, in well-nourished patients at least, recovery usually follows about 21 days after the initial infection.

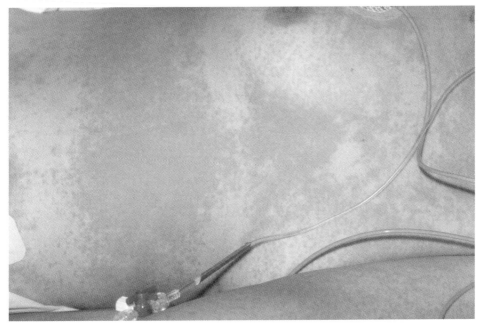

FIGURE 3.19 A measles rash seen here on the chest and upper arm of a patient.

Some cases of measles lead to serious complications. The initial viral infection results in a short-lived, general immunosuppression, which can allow secondary infections to develop. It is these infections that are responsible for a large number of the deaths that occur after an infection with the measles virus. Occasionally (once in every 3000 infections), a lymphocyte that has been infected with the measles virus enters the brain. Measles virus is able to replicate in the brain, and this leads to acute post-infectious encephalitis (brain inflammation). This condition can be fatal, or can cause severe and permanent brain damage. An even rarer complication is a brain infection known as subacute sclerosing panencephalitis (SSPE). SSPE does not occur immediately, but is a slow infection that takes 6–8 years to become apparent. In common with the slow infections caused by prions (see Chapter 4), SSPE is a progressive, fatal neurodegenerative disease. It develops in about one in a million individuals who have measles early on in life, usually before they reach the age of two. SSPE is believed to be due to the presence of a mutant form of the measles virus.

Worldwide there are an estimated 0.9 million deaths each year from measles, and the majority of these fatalities occur in developing countries where measles is widespread. Children become infected very early in their lives, and many subsequently die. The mortality (death rate) due to measles in African children of less than four years of age is 42%. As we suggested above, malnutrition is a major contributory factor to this grim statistic. An attenuated measles vaccine is available, and has been used very successfully, almost eliminating the disease in countries such as the USA and UK. In the UK, the measles vaccine is administered as part of the MMR (measles, mumps and rubella) vaccination. Recent fears concerning the safety of this vaccination has led to a drop in the number of children being immunized.

○ Suggest what will happen to the prevalence of measles in the UK.

● It will increase among members of the unvaccinated population.

3.6.2 What makes a particular virus strain a pathogen?

Earlier, you may have been puzzled to learn that two very similar smallpox viruses produced very different symptoms in their hosts. This demonstrates how closely related viruses may differ in their virulence. Determining the exact cause of such differences is not easy.

○ Can you think of any reasons why?

● In viral infections, the symptoms are often the result of the host immune response. Establishing the contribution of various components to disease symptoms is difficult, since even if a substance has a clear-cut activity *in vitro*, it may be hard to demonstrate the same activity *in vivo* (see Section 1.1). You may have thought of some other good reasons too.

Despite the difficulties, four key areas where change affects viral virulence have been identified: overcoming host defences, spreading within a host and between hosts, replication, and production of substances that are directly toxic to the host.

Summary of Section 3.6

1   Viruses can cause acute or persistent infections.

2   Persistent infections can be latent, when the virus is essentially dormant until it is reactivated, or slow, when the virus replicates only very slowly.

3   Some viruses transform host cells and may give rise to cancers.

4   Smallpox virus is transmitted by the respiratory route. It causes a mild primary viraemia, then a secondary viraemia with characteristic skin symptoms. It has a high mortality.

5   Measles virus is also spread by the respiratory route and also gives rise to two viraemias. The symptoms include a skin rash and Koplik's spots. Measles can have severe complications, which can themselves lead to death.

6   Very similar viruses can produce very different diseases.

3.7 New and emerging viral diseases

An emerging virus may be a newcomer to a particular population, or it may be an existing pathogen that is infecting a growing number of people. Alternatively, an emerging virus might be one that has been undetectable before, until new techniques have brought it to light. We look at some examples below.

3.7.1 Ebola virus

Ebola virus belongs to a family of negative strand RNA viruses called filoviruses, and causes a type of disease known as a viral **haemorrhagic fever**. These fevers are often fatal, and are characterized by muscle pain, headaches, local or general haemorrhaging, circulatory shock and death. The Ebola virus first caused recorded disease in humans in 1976 in Zaire and Sudan, following new exploration and exploitation of the jungle, when around 600 people were infected and over 400 died. Many episodes of human Ebola infection have occurred since, mostly in Africa, but apart from a 1995 outbreak in Zaire, they have been small in scale. Ebola virus infections have also occurred in the UK, USA, and Russia, but these have been laboratory-acquired infections.

Ebola virus received so much publicity during the 1990s that it has become something of a stereotype for emerging diseases as 'something nasty from the jungle'. There is little doubt that Ebola comes from the jungle, as people living and working in the rainforest are often the first to become infected. Ebola is a zoonosis, and surprisingly, the animal that carries Ebola, the **reservoir of infection**, has never been found. It must exist however, because Ebola virus is not endemic in the human population. Knowing the source of a virus is a crucial step in helping to prevent human infections, and the mysterious origins of Ebola only serve to make it more terrifying. However, the tabloid nightmare of an Ebola plague arriving in the West on board a plane is unlikely, since the virus is transmitted by direct contact rather than through the air, and is not particularly contagious.

3.7.2 Hantavirus pulmonary syndrome

In 1993 healthy, young, Navajo Indians began to die of a mysterious disease in the Four Corners area of New Mexico, USA. The illness started abruptly with fever, muscle aches and headache and progressed rapidly to respiratory failure caused by an accumulation of fluid in the lungs. The authorities quickly identified a new type of hantavirus as the cause. Hantaviruses belong to the family Bunyaviridae and have negative strand RNA genomes packaged into helical, enveloped capsids. A pathogenic hantavirus had not been reported in the USA before, but hantaviruses had been linked with renal diseases in Europe and Asia.

Hantaviruses are known to be endemic in rodents all over the world, and are shed from these animals in saliva, urine and faeces. In these rodents, which are the natural hosts of hantaviruses, the viruses cause little or no disease, but if they cross species into humans, the effects can be devastating. Once the infectious agent for the American pulmonary disease was identified, the search began for the rodent reservoir. The culprit was found to be the deer mouse, which was common in the area. Further investigations revealed that the deer mouse population had undergone a recent surge, caused partly by an increase in its food supply. Many patients reported exposure to the mice, either in the external environment or as pests in their homes. It was discovered that the mouse excrement, urine or saliva could be converted into an aerosol form which, when unwittingly inhaled, caused the pulmonary disease. This understanding of the causes of hantavirus pulmonary syndrome has led to effective preventative methods, such as rodent-proofing of dwellings and prompt disinfection of any mouse urine or faeces.

3.7.3 Hepatitis C

If an infection results in inflammation of the liver it is known as hepatitis. Nine different viruses are now (2002) known to cause hepatitis, with the hepatitis B virus probably being the best known. Hepatitis B can cause serious liver disease, including one form of liver cancer, hepatocellular carcinoma. Another virus that is tropic for the liver is hepatitis A, which is usually contracted by the faecal–oral route; however, both hepatitis A and (especially) hepatitis B can be transmitted by blood transfusion. In the 1970s, 90% of hepatitis occurring in transfusion recipients was found to be non-A and non-B-type (NANB) hepatitis. Chiron Corporation (a pharmaceutical company) found one of the agents responsible for NANB hepatitis in the late 1980s, using molecular cloning technology (see Section 3.8). These techniques allowed them to detect an RNA molecule that turned out to be a viral genome, in the blood of a chimpanzee with NANB hepatitis. The viral genome comprised 10 000 nucleotides of (+) RNA, and when it was sequenced it was found to be a member of the Flaviviridae family. This new type of virus was called hepatitis C, and no attempts to grow it in artificial culture have succeeded, which explains why it was not discovered before.

In this section we have examined three new diseases that have emerged for different reasons.

☐ What are these reasons?

⬤ Ebola virus occurred when humans exploited new environments, disturbing the balance of natural host–virus relationships. Pulmonary hantavirus was brought about by an increasing deer mouse population and the subsequent infiltration of homes, and finally hepatitis C remained undetected until the technology was available to find it in the blood.

Summary of Section 3.7

1 New viral diseases often emerge following a disturbance in the ecological balance.

2 Some new viral diseases can only be identified when new molecular technology allows their detection.

3.8 The good that viruses do

Viruses are very important pathogens, but we have also used them to our own advantage. Bacteriophages have been of immense importance in the development of the science of genetics, including the identification of DNA as the genetic material. Bacteriophages are easily grown and have provided us with a great deal of general information about viruses. Today, they are used in **recombinant DNA technology**, which is the creation of new DNA molecules using pieces of DNA from different sources. In this case, pieces of non-phage DNA are incorporated into a phage genome, to give a recombinant DNA molecule. The altered phage is then allowed to infect a culture of bacteria so that, by allowing the viral replication cycle to proceed, many copies of the phage genome are obtained. Making many copies of a DNA molecule is known as **cloning** it, so the foreign DNA introduced into the phage genome is cloned and the phage genome itself is known as the **cloning vector**. The most important bacteriophage cloning vectors are M13 and lambda.

Bacteriophages have also been allies in our fight against pathogenic bacteria. In the pre-antibiotic era they were used therapeutically to treat bacterial infections such as cholera and typhoid fever.

○ Explain this therapeutic approach.

● The bacteriophages might infect the pathogenic bacteria, lysing them and relieving the infection.

To this end, bacteriophage cultures were administered topically (on the skin), inhaled, injected or swallowed, but the outcome was unpredictable and not always successful. When antibiotics became available, therapeutic phage research was largely abandoned, except in what was then the Soviet Union. Now that bacteria are becoming increasingly resistant to our antibiotics, interest in bacteriophage therapy has been rekindled in the West. Several companies have even been set up in the USA to develop bacteriophage treatments. The hope is that bacteriophages may succeed in clearing bacterial infections when all the available antibiotics are ineffective.

Gene therapy, a novel medical technique that may allow genetic disorders to be treated, also uses viruses. Some genetic disorders are caused by the absence of a particular gene. Others, such as Duchenne muscular dystrophy, are caused by mutated single genes (the dystrophin gene, in this case). Gene therapy aims to supply an individual with a copy of a missing or dysfunctional gene, using viruses as delivery agents. Some viruses, such as retroviruses, incorporate DNA copies of their nucleic acid into the host genome. These viruses could be modified so that they carry a missing human gene and deliver it to the host genome. The specific tropisms of viruses could be exploited too in order to target particular tissues or organs. Gene therapy has been used successfully to replace a missing gene that caused an immune deficiency disease. A sample of the patient's cells was removed, supplied with the missing gene using a modified retrovirus, and then replaced. So far, there has been only limited therapeutic success using this technique, but hopes for the future are high.

Summary of Section 3.8

Viruses have been useful to humans in the following ways:

1 as a tool for basic research;

2 as therapeutic agents for bacterial diseases;

3 as vectors for gene therapy.

Learning outcomes for Chapter 3

When you have studied this chapter, you should be able to:

3.1 Define and use, or recognize definitions and applications of, each of the terms printed in **bold** in the text. (*all Section 3 questions*)

3.2 Outline the history of the discovery and study of viruses. (*Question 3.1*)

3.3 Discuss the nature and origin of viruses. (*Question 3.2*)

3.4 Describe, using named examples, the different classes of viruses. (*Question 3.3*)

3.5 Outline the steps of a general viral replication cycle, and give specific named examples of each step. (*Question 3.4*)

3.6 Describe the effects that viruses can have at the cellular level. (*Question 3.5*)

3.7 Using named examples, describe the effects of viral diseases on the host. (*Question 3.6*)

3.8 Give examples of newly emerging viral diseases. (*Question 3.7*)

3.9 Outline some ways in which viruses are beneficial to humans. (*Question 3.8*)

Questions for Chapter 3

Question 3.1

What were the two most important pieces of equipment used to identify viruses?

Question 3.2

State three differences between the genomes of viruses and bacteria that suggest that viruses did *not* evolve from prokaryotes.

Question 3.3

Give one advantage and one disadvantage of the Baltimore viral classification system.

Question 3.4

Compare and contrast the replication strategies of variola major and adenovirus.

Question 3.5

(a) What are the possible cytopathic effects of viral infection? (b) Are any of these changes seen following infection with cytocidal viruses?

Question 3.6

Several viral infections give rise to skin rashes, and the exact appearance of the rash is often important for diagnosis. Match the list of skin disorders (A–E) with infections by either (a) the measles virus or (b) the smallpox virus.

A Koplick's spots   D macules

B pustules   E vesicles

C papules

Question 3.7

What is a haemorrhagic fever, and how does it kill a patient? Give one example of a recently emerged viral haemorrhagic fever.

Question 3.8

In a short paragraph, explain what bacteriophages are and how they may be used therapeutically.

4 PRIONS

4.1 The nature of prions

The term **prion** is derived from their description as *pr*oteinaceous *in*fectious particles, and unlike any other infectious agents, prions have no nucleic acid. The exact nature of prions is still unknown, but they appear to consist entirely of protein. Prions give rise to a group of fatal, neurodegenerative diseases called **transmissible spongiform encephalopathies** (TSEs). These diseases produce characteristic lesions in the brain, giving the tissue a sponge-like appearance upon microscopical examination (see Figure 4.1 overleaf). TSEs are characterized by lengthy incubation periods (10–30 years for human TSEs), and because of this they are also known as 'slow diseases'. Do not confuse these with the viral slow infections that you met in Chapter 3.

Prion proteins are rogue versions of a group of proteins, known as PrP^c (pronounced 'pee-are-pee-see'), found in mammals and birds. These proteins are small (M_r 33 000–35 000) membrane glycoproteins, and while they are expressed on most cells, they are found in greatest abundance in the brain. PrP^c protein is essential for TSEs to develop. Mice genetically engineered to lack the PrP^c gene do not develop TSE infection after inoculation with material that produces TSE disease in mice that have a functional PrP^c gene. An unusual property of PrP^c protein is that protein molecules with identical amino acid sequences can fold up in different ways, to give proteins with different conformations. One of these conformations (PrP^c) represents the functional protein, and is usually the only form present, while the other (PrP^{sc}) is a rogue version, or prion. Exactly what causes this conformational switch isn't always clear, but a number of TSEs have been found to have a genetic component, which results in the production of only the PrP^{sc} protein. However, these diseases are hereditary and not infectious, and make up only a fraction of TSE cases. What is clear, is that once PrP^{sc} is present in a normal host, the functional PrP^c protein becomes folded into the same conformation as the prion protein and acquires its properties. In this way PrP^{sc} is able to 'replicate', and accumulate into the protein aggregates found in brains with TSEs. This ability of protein to replicate itself without the need for DNA has been called 'protein inheritance', and explains how prion proteins can function as infectious agents.

One might expect a proteinaceous infectious agent to be easily inactivated, but surprisingly, prion proteins have markedly different chemical properties from the normally folded protein. Whereas PrP^c proteins are degraded by protease enzymes and are soluble in mild detergents, prion proteins (PrP^{sc}) resist degradation by proteases and are insoluble in detergents. Resistance to the bacterial protease Proteinase K is a feature of PrP^{sc}, and is used as a marker for TSEs. Prion protein is actually notoriously difficult to inactivate, even using sterilization treatments that kill, or inactivate, all other known organisms and pathogens. Interestingly, there is no immune response in TSE diseases, even though prion proteins are large enough to qualify as antigens.

Conventionally, genes are written in *italics* (as in *PrP^c*), but the protein they encode is written in roman font (PrP^c).

○ Why might this be?

◖ Prion proteins are either derived from the host itself, or resemble the host PrP^c protein so closely that they cannot be identified as non-self.

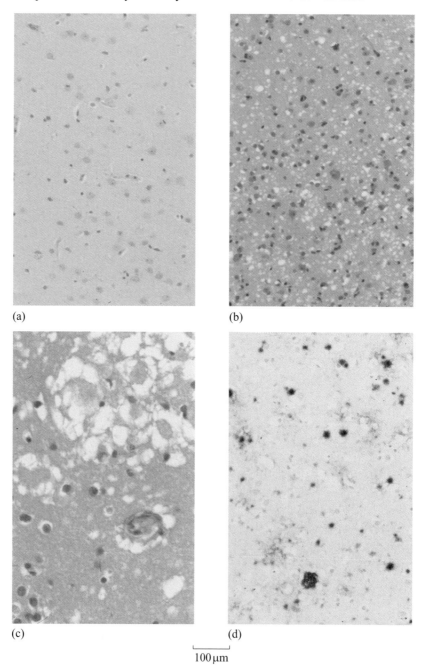

(a)   (b)

(c)   (d)

|—————|
100 μm

FIGURE 4.13 (a) Thin section through a normal human cerebral cortex, stained with haematoxylin and eosin. (b) Thin section through the cerebral cortex of an individual with the original form of CJD. Note the widespread spongiform changes and the multiple small vacuoles in the grey matter. (c) Thin section through the cerebral cortex of an individual with variant CJD, showing local spongiform changes associated with numerous plaques. (d) Prion protein in the cerebral cortex of an individual infected with variant CJD. Note the densely stained rounded amyloid plaques and numerous, widespread, amorphous prion protein deposits, identified by staining with a prion-specific antibody (brown).

4.2 A history of prion diseases

The best characterized TSE is scrapie, a disease of sheep and goats, which has been known in Europe for at least two centuries. The scrapie agent has been studied extensively, and has provided much of the information known about prions. Animals suffering from scrapie have difficulty walking and suffer itching to such an extent that they may rub themselves raw, hence the name scrapie. Although the disorder was long suspected to be infectious, it wasn't until 1936 that the first experimental sheep-to-sheep transmission was achieved. This was done by injecting spinal cord homogenate from a diseased sheep into a healthy animal, satisfying the last of Koch's postulates. The same year, brain homogenates from scrapie-infected sheep were shown to retain their infectivity after passage through filters too small to allow anything except viruses through. However, the inability to completely purify the infectious agent, even with modern techniques, makes their unequivocal identification impossible. Examination of partially purified prion material under the electron microscope reveals rod-shaped **fibrils** (small fibres) of various shapes and sizes. These fibrils are not destroyed by treatment with nuclease enzymes, and in fact are aggregates of prion protein. They provide a morphological marker for scrapie infection or disease (see Figure 4.2).

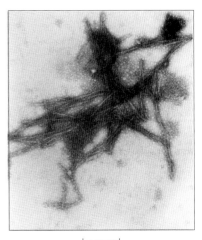

150 nm

FIGURE 4.2
Fibrils of prion protein from the brain of a scrapie-infected mouse.

The first TSEs to affect humans were identified in the 1920s by Creutzfeldt and Jakob. The most common of these diseases is now known as Creutzfeldt–Jakob disease or CJD, which mostly affects middle-aged people. Patients with this disease suffer rapid dementia and other neurological disorders, usually dying within 4–8 months from the onset of symptoms. Other related diseases have subsequently been described: Gerstmann–Straussler–Scheinker syndrome in the 1930s, kuru in the 1950s, variant CJD in the 1980s and fatal familial insomnia in the 1990s.

Summary of Sections 4.1 and 4.2

1   Prions are abnormally folded molecules of a membrane glycoprotein.

2   Prions spread by corrupting normal protein molecules to the abnormal conformation.

3   Prions cause transmissible spongiform encephalopathies (TSEs).

4   Animal TSEs have been known for centuries, but human TSEs have been identified only relatively recently.

4.3 Transmission of TSE infectious agents

Although TSEs can all be transmitted experimentally, not all of them are naturally infectious. Gerstmann–Straussler–Scheinker syndrome and fatal familial insomnia are inherited disorders. In inherited TSEs, the victims have non-sex-linked dominant mutations of the PrP^c gene, and this increases their susceptibility to developing TSEs. Creutzfeldt–Jakob disease has several different aetiologies (causes). About 90% of CJD cases are described as **sporadic**, which means they are isolated, unrelated cases. Sporadic cases affect one in a million of the population per year. Around 10% of CJD cases are inherited and less than 1% are acquired iatrogenically (as a result of medical treatment). Iatrogenic CJD results from the receipt of material derived from a CJD sufferer. This material may be in the form of grafts, e.g. corneal grafts, or hormones, e.g. growth hormone purified from the brains of cadavers. Prion proteins are not destroyed by standard hospital sterilization procedures, so CJD and other prion diseases could be contracted from fomites such as surgical instruments. This has led to the use of disposable instruments for some procedures.

Scrapie, kuru, bovine spongiform encephalopathy (BSE) and variant CJD appear to be infectious diseases. The scrapie agent can be transmitted from ewe to lamb, but this is thought to occur by routes other than *in utero*.

○ Is this horizontal or vertical transmission?

◉ Infection *in utero* would be vertical transmission, so most ewe to lamb infections are probably horizontal.

However, a placenta from a ewe with scrapie can be a source of infection on farms. Within flocks, scrapie seems to affect related animals. The scrapie agent appears to have been transmitted to mink fed on infected sheep heads, as mink fed in this way went on to develop so-called transmissible mink encephalopathy. However, although humans have eaten scrapie-infected meat, including neural tissues, for at least 200 years, there are no records (in 2002) of any TSEs developing in humans as a result.

The transmission of kuru is probably the best understood of the TSEs. This disease was found solely in the Fore tribe of New Guinea, and was a major cause of death among the tribe's people in the 1960s, when more than 10% of the population succumbed. It was passed from person to person by cannibalistic practices. In this culture, it was customary to eat deceased relatives, with women and children consuming brain and nervous tissues. It has been speculated that at one such ritual, the deceased had sporadic CJD. Those who consumed tissues from this person contracted kuru, though why such individuals should develop kuru and not CJD itself is unclear. The name kuru means shivering or trembling, which was the main symptom of the disease. Once cannabalism was abandoned, the disease declined and the last kuru victim died in 1998.

The full story of TSEs has yet to be uncovered, and there are still scientists who do not believe in prions, but think that TSEs are the result of unknown viruses with unusual properties. Another view is that TSEs are caused by a ubiquitous conventional infectious agent, which only causes disease in a few genetically susceptible individuals.

○ In this argument, why would such an unknown infectious agent need to be ubiquitous?

◉ To demonstrate the presence of a disease agent, diseased and healthy tissues are compared. Perhaps the infectious agent goes undetected because it occurs in all tissues, regardless of disease status.

Yet another theory suggests that **virinos** are responsible. These hypothetical agents are described as scrapie-specific nucleic acids coated with PrP^{sc}. The nucleic acid would probably not be expressed as protein, but still be involved in the disease process.

Summary of Section 4.3

1   Most CJD cases are sporadic, though 10% may be inherited and 1% iatrogenic in origin.

2   TSE-infected tissue is a source of infection, although not all TSEs are infectious in normal circumstances.

3   The best understood example of a human TSE is kuru, where infection was transmitted through cannibalism.

4   There is still some controversy about the role of PrP^{sc} in TSEs.

4.4 The political prion

BSE has been a terrible tragedy in the UK, both for farmers and the families of those with variant CJD. By the autumn of 2001, 98 people were dead or dying of variant CJD and the numbers have kept on rising. BSE did affect cattle in other countries, particularly Switzerland and Ireland, but the scale of these epidemics was nowhere near as large as that in the UK.

BSE was first detected in UK cattle in 1986, but it is now believed to have been infecting cattle as long ago as the 1970s and early 1980s. It can only be speculated why these early cases were missed. The disease was unknown at the time, and may have occurred in isolated cases, or the infected cattle may still have been incubating the disease at the time of slaughter. It was the practice at the time to recycle abattoir wastes into animal feeds. This practice might seem abhorrent, but is a cost-effective way of using material unsuitable for human consumption. Originally, it was believed that material in cattle feed made from scrapie-infected sheep was the source of infection. This hypothesis has since been rejected, and the source of infection is now thought to have been a novel prion mutation in cattle, or sheep. This novel TSE agent is believed to have emerged in the early 1970s and gradually spread through cattle stock via recycled *bovine* material in their food.

BSE was first recognized in dairy cows, and by 1992 around 1% of all adult cattle in the UK were infected. The Government response to the BSE crisis was slow because it was widely believed that BSE posed no risk to human health. Ministers, officials and the scientific advisory committees were all more concerned that the public would be alarmed by BSE and an economically damaging food scare would result. It wasn't until July 1988 that it was made illegal to feed ruminant-derived protein to ruminants in the UK. This removed the main source of infection and was successful in the long term. In 1993, at the peak of the epidemic, 1000 new cases of BSE were being reported every week, but by April 1996 the number of BSE cases reported had shrunk to less than 1200 a month. At this point, the measures taken in the UK were aimed at reducing the risk posed to cattle. It wasn't until September 1990 that specific cattle tissues such as brain and spinal cord were banned for consumption by humans, livestock and poultry. Worryingly, it is estimated that before 1995, nearly one million BSE-infected cattle may have ended up in the human food chain. Also in 1990 the government set up a National CJD surveillance unit, and in 1996 they identified a new form of CJD. Variant CJD (vCJD), as it is called, particularly affects younger people and differs from ordinary CJD in its clinical profile and pattern of brain damage. In March of that year the Government admitted that BSE had in all likelihood been transmitted to humans as variant CJD. The link between BSE and CJD has only recently been clearly established, but it is of note that most of the cases of variant CJD have occurred in Britain, where the incidence of BSE was by far the greatest.

○ If people were infected before 1995, when might CJD symptoms appear?

▪ TSEs are slow infections, so a peak of disease might not be apparent until 2020–2040.

In January 1998, the BSE Inquiry was set up by the Government to analyse the events surrounding the emergence of BSE and variant CJD. It concluded that Government policy decisions such as the ruminant feed ban were appropriate, but had often been taken too late and not enforced rigorously enough.

Summary of Section 4.4

1   The BSE outbreak was caused by animal feeding practices that were driven by economic considerations.

2   The Government's response was criticized as 'too little, too late'.

3   Variant CJD is thought to be a result of eating BSE-infected cattle.

4   The full scale of the BSE epidemic may not be known for many years.

Learning outcomes for Chapter 4

When you have studied this chapter, you should be able to:

4.1   Define and use, or recognize definitions and applications of, each of the terms printed in **bold** in the text. (*Questions 4.1 and 4.2*)

4.2   Describe the molecular nature of a prion and explain how this agent causes disease. (*Questions 4.1 and 4.2*)

4.3   Describe the transmission of named TSEs. (*Questions 4.1 and 4.2*)

4.4   Outline the main events of the BSE outbreak in the UK in the 1980s–1990s. (*Question 4.2*)

Questions for Chapter 4

Question 4.1

Suppose that a hypothetical condition, mad dog disease (MDD), is starting to appear among domestic pet dogs. Describe the kinds of evidence that might lead you to believe that MDD is a TSE caused by a prion.

Question 4.2

Dog carcases are usually destroyed by incineration, but an unscrupulous dog food manufacturer believes that they could be economically recycled into dog food. Assuming the scenario in Question 4.1, how would you advise the government on this matter?

5 THE PROTOCTISTS

5.1 The nature and naming of protoctists

Protoctists are eukaryotic organisms that are either single-celled or have only simple multicellular structures. The Protoctista include organisms of diverse origins, such as those that make up most of the oceans' plankton, the amoebae and the algae (including seaweeds). This kingdom originally gave rise to plants, animals and fungi, but today's protoctists probably bear little resemblance to these first eukaryotes, since they have had millions of years in which to evolve. The protoctists now comprise those eukaryotes that cannot be classified as plants, animals or fungi, and not surprisingly therefore this kingdom exhibits extraordinary diversity, having 30 or so phyla (major groups). In comparison, the plant kingdom has only 12 phyla, and although the number of animal phyla (29) is about the same as the number of protoctist phyla, there is more genetic diversity in the single protoctist phylum Ciliophora, than in the whole of the animal kingdom! The extraordinary variety of structures found in the Protoctista ranges from microscopic organisms to sea kelps 60 m long.

Water is an absolute requirement for survival and growth, and many protoctists are found in freshwater or saltwater, while others inhabit the soil, and some live as symbionts in plants, animals and fungi. Protoctists vary widely in their modes of nutrition, with some able to photosynthesize like plants, while others are heterotrophs and feed on other organisms or dead material. The reproductive strategies of the protoctists are very varied and may involve alternating sexual and asexual generations. If an organism has both a sexual and an asexual life cycle, it is often the environmental conditions that determine which type of reproduction predominates. If conditions are favourable for growth and replication, the asexual cycle frequently predominates, whereas in less favourable conditions, the sexual cycle may be more common. Finally, there are other protoctists that have not been observed to reproduce sexually at all!

Many parasitic protoctists form special, thick-walled, highly resistant structures called **cysts**, in a process called **encystment**. Such cysts serve a number of purposes: they protect the organism from adverse environmental conditions, they provide shelter for reproductive processes and they allow transmission of the parasite from one host to another. Some protoctists can survive as cysts for a very long time, so transmission of the parasite to a new host can occur a long time after leaving the previous one. At some point, **excystment** occurs; this is when the cyst releases the vegetative form of the parasite, known as a **trophozoite**. Ingesting cysts is a common way in which humans become infected with these parasites, and excystment frequently takes place in the intestine.

Despite the variety of forms and modes of life, there is one structure found in most protoctists for at least one stage of their life cycle, and that is one or more flagella. The flagella are used in feeding, locomotion, etc. and are distinct from the flagella found on bacteria, which have a different structure, and function by a different mechanism. Protoctists that possess flagella during the 'adult' stage of their life cycles are colloquially known as **flagellates**. These animal-like cells have one or more flagella and include *Giardia* spp., which cause diarrhoea, and the trypanosomes, which cause sleeping sickness. However, even though these groups both have flagella, they are not related to one another.

Single-celled protoctists that have animal-like cells and are unable to photosynthesize, are sometimes referred to as **protozoa**, but this is not a discrete classification, since (like flagellates) its members have diverse evolutionary origins. Protozoan cells have one or more nuclei and are usually classified according to their cell structures: for example, members of the phylum Apicomplexa all have an arrangement of organelles known as the *api*cal *complex* (see below). It is largely the animal-like protoctists, which are found in both free-living and parasitic forms, that are human pathogens. Although few in number, they cause some of our most serious diseases. You already know about malaria, which is one of these diseases, as you have studied it in Book 1; below we consider the other major pathogenic protoctists. One reason why protoctist-mediated diseases have such serious consequences is that there are few really effective drugs to treat them.

○ Table 5.1 shows some drugs used against protoctists, and briefly describes their mode of action. Can you suggest why anti-protoctist therapy is often unsuccessful?

⬤ Protoctists are eukaryotes, so have the same type of molecules and metabolism as their hosts. Thus it is difficult to achieve selective toxicity.

Note that some of the drugs used are folic acid antagonists. Protoctists are unable to absorb folic acid from their host, so they are sensitive to inhibition of their own folic acid metabolism, although their hosts are not, because we can take up folic acid from the diet. Likewise, melarsoprol, a drug based on arsenic, inhibits an enzyme found only in protoctists. However other drugs, such as those that bind to DNA and disrupt its structure, affect host cells too, and rely for their efficacy on subtle differences between host and pathogen, such as different rates of drug uptake.

TABLE 5.1 Some commonly used anti-protoctist drugs.

Drug	Mechanism of action	Disease treated
metronidazole	metabolized to yield a molecule that interacts with DNA	giardiasis, amoebiasis
suramin	inhibits enzymes involved in ATP synthesis	African trypanosomiasis
pentamidine	binds to DNA	trypanosomiasis (all)
melarsoprol	arsenic compound that inactivates thiol (–SH) groups	*gambiense* trypanosomiasis
tinidazole	inhibits glucose metabolism and interferes with mitochondrial function	*E. histolytica* amoebiasis
benzimidazole	inhibits glucose metabolism and interferes with mitochondrial function	Chagas' disease
iodoquinol	blocks DNA replication	*E. histolytica* amoebiasis
paromomycin	blocks ribosomal activity	*E. histolytica* amoebiasis; cryptosporidiosis
propamidine	binds to DNA	*Acanthamoeba* amoebiasis; *gambiense* trypanosomiasis
pyrimethamine	folic acid antagonist	toxoplasmosis
sulfadiazine	folic acid antagonist	toxoplasmosis
spiramycin	blocks ribosome activity	toxoplasmosis
clindamycin	blocks ribosome activity	toxoplasmosis

Summary of Section 5.1

1   Protoctists are eukaryotic organisms, and are taxonomically and structurally highly diverse.

2   Almost all protoctists have flagella, and those in which flagella are present in the dominant stage are known as flagellates.

3   Single-celled protoctists that cannot photosynthesize are known as protozoa.

4   Few protoctists are pathogens, but those that are cause serious diseases.

5   It is difficult to treat diseases caused by protoctists, as it is hard to achieve selective toxicity.

5.2 Giardiasis

Flagellated protoctists that cause the chronic diarrhoea known as **giardiasis** belong to the genus *Giardia*. These organisms were discovered by Vilein Lambl in 1885, and may have been seen even earlier by van Leeuwenhoek, but they were not recognized as pathogens until the 1960s. More than 40 species have now been recorded all over the world, but humans are usually infected by *Giardia lamblia*. (Note that this organism appears as *Giardia duodenalis* or *Giardia intestinalis* in some texts.) The genus *Giardia* is very ancient in evolutionary terms, and, interestingly, *Giardia* spp. have no mitochondria. As you will see, each stage in the life cycle of *G. lamblia* is finely tuned to its environment.

◯   From what you have learned so far, do you think *Giardia* have always been parasites?

◕   The protoctists are extremely ancient and evolved long before the mammals. Therefore it is likely that the *Giardia* were free-living in the past and have only recently adapted to the mammalian gut.

The organisms enter the body as cysts (which have four nuclei) in food or water contaminated with faeces from humans or other mammals. Following ingestion, excystment is triggered by the low pH in the stomach, although the trophozoites (feeding stage, with two nuclei each; see Figure 5.1) do not emerge until the duodenum is reached.

◯   Suggest why the trophozoites do not emerge in the stomach.

◕   The gastric acid would kill them.

Emergence in the small intestine is stimulated by the increase in pH and by the proteases found in the duodenum. The pear-shaped trophozoites then use their four pairs of flagella to swim through the liquid of the small intestine, and to attach to the mucus coating of the gut epithelium. Some trophozoites penetrate the mucus layer and, using specific receptors and their sucking pads, attach to the epithelia of the duodenum and jejunum (the upper and middle part of the small intestine, respectively).

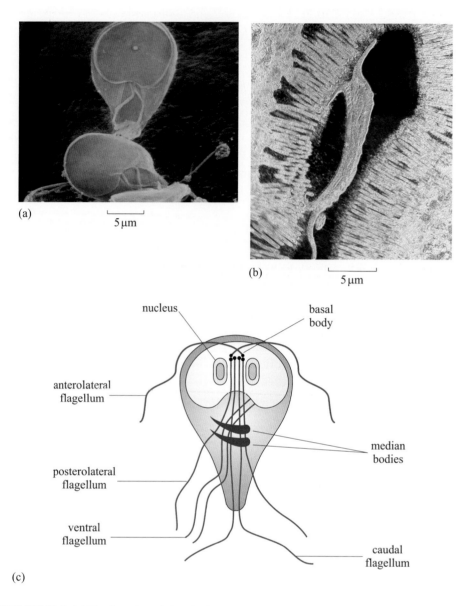

FIGURE 5.1 (a) Trophozoites of *Giardia lamblia*. The flagella are clearly visible. (b) *Giardia* trophozoite attached to the intestinal epithelium. (c) Diagram of a *Giardia* trophozoite showing the two nuclei and four pairs of flagella.

Once the trophozoites are attached, they multiply by binary fission and may reach sufficient numbers to disrupt the absorption of fat from the intestine. A week or two after infection, this results in loose, fatty, stools with an offensive smell. Over time, this diarrhoea may lead to weight loss and anaemia.

If trophozoites are carried to the far end of the small intestine, the increase in pH and a high bile concentration trigger encystment. If encystment did not occur, the trophozoites would die, since they cannot survive outside the host under normal conditions. An encysting trophozoite lays down a thick, fibrous protein coat around itself and undergoes one round of asexual reproduction inside, to give four nuclei.

The cysts, which persist in freshwater at 4 °C and above, are then discharged in the faeces, and as few as ten of them are required to infect another individual.

Giardiasis is particularly common in children in developing countries, but it does also infect the children of rich countries, especially those in day nurseries. The cysts can remain active in soil for several months and are able to withstand the concentrations of chlorine used to disinfect drinking water. Giardiasis may be treated with the antiprotoctist drug metronidazole (see Table 5.1), and cysts can be removed from drinking water by filtration, although this is not always economically possible.

Summary of Section 5.2

1   Giardiasis is a chronic diarrhoea caused by *Giardia lamblia*.

2   Giardiasis is passed on by cysts in infected water or food.

3   *Giardia* cysts are resistant to water chlorination, but can be removed by filtration.

5.3 Trypanosomiasis

Unicellular, animal-like cells with flagella, known as trypanosomes, cause **trypanosomiasis** or sleeping sickness. Unlike *Giardia*, these parasites have a complex life cycle involving more than one type of host and an insect vector. Trypanosomiasis causes chronic diseases that occur in Africa and tropical and subtropical America.

In African sleeping sickness, cattle and wild animals are the reservoirs of infection. The trypanosomes reach humans when they are bitten by tsetse flies (Figure 5.2) that have fed on infected animals or people (Figure 5.3 overleaf). The parasites soon reach the bloodstream and start to multiply. There are two types of African sleeping sickness caused by different subspecies of *Trypanosoma brucei*. In the East African savanna, the disease is caused by *Trypanosoma brucei rhodesiense*, while in the rainforests of west and central Africa, *Trypanosoma brucei gambiense* is responsible. The two trypanosomes attack the body in different ways. Subspecies *rhodesiense* causes inflammation of the lymph nodes and kills the cells in the small blood vessels that supply the heart and brain. This infection can kill a person within a year, but subspecies *gambiense* takes around three years to cause death. It enters the central nervous system (CNS), causing the typical lethargy that gives the disease its name.

FIGURE 5.2
A tsetse fly, the vector of the African trypanosomes.

The African trypanosomes have an outer protein coat, the composition of which they can vary, so their antigenic properties change. This leaves the immune system continually one step behind, and rules out any hopes of a vaccine. You will learn more about the interaction of trypanosomes and the immune system from the Immunogy CD material associated with Book 3. African sleeping sickness can be treated with the drugs suramin and pentamidine, or melarsoprol if the CNS is involved.

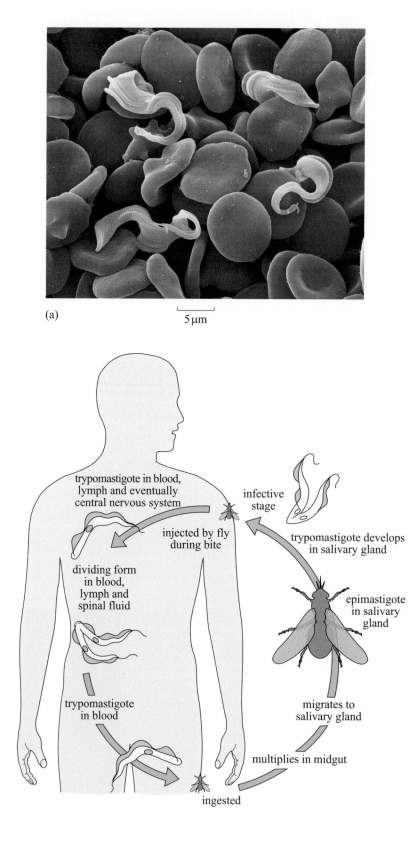

FIGURE 5.3

(a) Trypomastigotes (infective stage) of *Trypanosoma brucei rhodesiense* in mouse blood. (b) Life cycle of *T. brucei*. Infected domestic and wild animals form a large reservoir of infection.

FIGURE 5.4 A reduviid bug (actual size) from South America.

American trypanosomiasis is also known as Chagas' disease and affects around 12 million people in Central and South America. It has been speculated that Charles Darwin suffered from this disease for many years, following his adventures in South America. Trypanosomiasis is caused by *Trypanosoma cruzi*, which enters the blood in the bite of an infected reduviid bug (Figure 5.4), also called the 'kissing bug' because it often bites around the mouth. The kissing bug is also renowned for defaecating in the wound from which it has just fed. The trypanosome is shed in the bug's faeces and introduced into the body through the wound. Alternatively, the faeces remain on the skin until, in response to the irritation the bite causes, the victim rubs them into the bite wound. The parasites enter the lymph nodes, spleen, liver and CNS. They also travel to the muscles and mononuclear phagocyte system, where they shed their outer membranes along with their flagella and round up, forming a structure known as an amastigote. These then reproduce in the muscles, causing the muscle cells to rupture, releasing the progeny into the blood as trypomastigotes (the infective stage). Any reduviid bug that feeds on this person may now carry the trypomastigotes to a new host. The most common cause of death in Chagas' disease is heart failure, since the trypanosomes infect this organ and cause considerable damage (see Figure 5.5 overleaf). There is no treatment for Chagas' disease, but drugs such as benzimidazole have been found to ease the condition.

Summary of Section 5.3

1   Trypanosomes cause African sleeping sickness and, in Central and South America, Chagas' disease.

2   Trypanosomes have a complex life cycle involving other hosts and an insect vector.

3   Trypanosomes can vary the antigens in their protein coats.

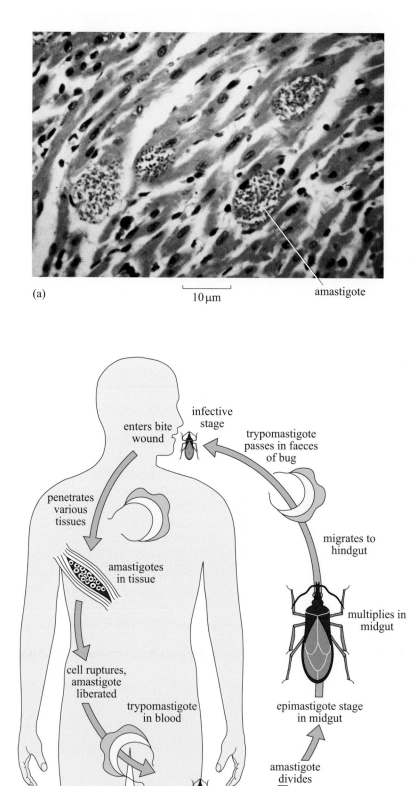

(a)

10 μm

amastigote

infective
stage

trypomastigote
passes in faeces
of bug

enters bite
wound

penetrates
various
tissues

migrates to
hindgut

amastigotes
in tissue

multiplies in
midgut

cell ruptures,
amastigote
liberated

trypomastigote
in blood

epimastigote stage
in midgut

amastigote
divides

ingested

FIGURE 5.5

(a) Amastigotes of *Trypanosoma cruzi* in heart muscle. (b) life cycle of *T. cruzi*.

(b)

5.4 Amoebiasis

Amoebae are animal-like, single-celled protoctists that move and capture prey by means of cytoplasmic extensions known as pseudopodia. A few are pathogens, and the disease they cause is called **amoebiasis**. We look at some of the main culprits below.

5.4.1 *Entamoeba* amoebiasis

Entamoeba histolytica infections are endemic in warm climates with inadequate sanitation, and affect around 500 million people each year. Infections arise when the protoctist's cysts are ingested in faecally contaminated water or food. Once the cysts reach the far end of the small intestine, excystment takes place, producing metacysts that subsequently divide to give eight trophozoites or amoebae (see Figure 5.6 overleaf). These amoebae then travel to the large intestine where they multiply by binary fission. The amoebae may then simply colonize the intestine, and persist as harmless commensals, producing no symptoms in the carrier (route A).

Alternatively, they may invade the colonic mucosa, causing inflammation and giving rise to characteristic ulcers (Figure 5.7). This inflammation, known as **dysentery**, produces a profuse bloody diarrhoea that may contain pus and mucus, and be accompanied by abdominal cramps. Systemic spread of the amoebae can occur, sometimes without any obvious signs of dysentery, resulting in abscesses in the liver, lungs and brain. At some stage during an infection, amoebae in the large intestine encyst (Figure 5.6, route B). The highly resistant spherical cysts, 10–15 µm in diameter, are then shed in the faeces to infect other hosts. Asymptomatic carriers, in particular, are important sources of infection within their communities. When studied *in vitro*, *E. histolytica* produces an impressive range of virulence factors, including proteases, pore-forming proteins and collagenases; however, its pathogenicity *in vivo* is poorly understood. Like *Giardia*, *Entamoeba histolytica* has no mitochondria.

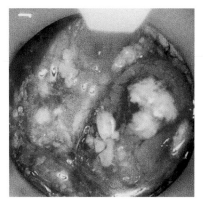

FIGURE 5.7
Amoebic colitis as seen by endoscopy. The white patches are ulcerated areas on the normal, pink colon wall. The disease is characterized by deep ulcers and an overlying smelly exudate.

Treatment for *Entamoeba histolytica* infection depends on how the disease develops. Metronidazole and tinidazole are used for amoebic dysentery and patients with liver abscesses. Asymptomatic carriers can be treated with iodoquinol or paromomycin. The parasite can be removed from the water supply by increasing the concentration of chlorine used for disinfection, or by using iodine instead.

5.4.2 *Acanthamoeba* amoebiasis

Species of *Acanthamoeba* are environmental amoebae, common in freshwater and moist soil, which can cause a brain infection called primary amoebic meningoencephalitis, as well as eye infections. Eye infections usually follow an injury, such as a foreign body in the eye or the damage caused by wearing contact lenses for long periods. These infections result in gradual ulceration of the cornea and **keratitis** (inflammation of the cornea), which can cause blindness. Effective antibiotic treatments for these eye infections have not yet been devised, since the amoebae are often resistant to the antibiotics in normal use. However, a combination of drugs that are more common as antibacterial antibiotics has been used with some success.

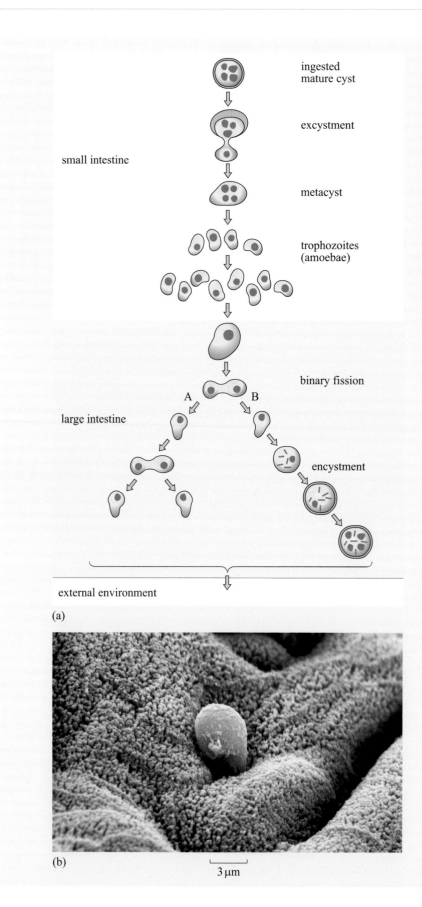

ingested
mature cyst

excystment

small intestine

metacyst

trophozoites
(amoebae)

binary fission

A   B

large intestine

encystment

external environment

(a)

(b)

3 μm

FIGURE 5.6

(a) Life cycle of *Entamoeba histolytica* in the gut. See text for details of routes A and B. (b) An *E. histolytica* trophozoite on the intestinal mucosa.

Summary of Section 5.4

1   Amoebiasis is caused by several species of amoeba.

2   *Entamoeba histolytica* causes amoebic dysentery and ulcerative colitis.

3   *Acanthamoeba* species can cause keratitis and, sometimes, primary amoebic meningoencephalitis.

5.5   The apicomplexans

These organisms belong to the the phylum Apicomplexa, and do not have flagella, except for the male gametes and the oocyst.

○   Recall from Section 5.1 the derivation of the name 'apicomplexans'.

●   They are named after the arrangement of organelles at one end of the cell, called the apical complex.

The apical complex is instrumental in achieving penetration into host cells, and all apicomplexans are in fact parasites of animal cells. They have very complex life cycles that alternate between sexual and asexual reproduction. Asexual reproduction produces many infective organisms via mitosis in a process called **schizogony**. Sexual reproduction involves the fusion of gametes to produce a zygote known as an **oocyst**, where infective spores are formed by meiosis in a process called **sporogony**. The life cycles may involve more than one host. The diseases they cause include toxoplasmosis and cryptosporidiosis. The *Plasmodium* parasites that cause malaria also belong to this group, and you have already studied these in a case study, so we do not deal with them here.

5.5.1   Toxoplasmosis

Toxoplasmosis is the name given to any infection with the parasite *Toxoplasma gondii*. This organism is found throughout the world in mammals and birds, but cats are the definitive hosts, since sexual reproduction of *T. gondii* is confined to them (see Figure 5.8a overleaf). Animals infected with *T. gondii* shed its cysts in their faeces, and these cysts can then infect other hosts. Humans may be infected via contaminated faeces or by eating infected animals that have been insufficiently cooked. The cysts gain entry through the mouth or nose and the resulting trophozoites colonize the intestine, so that further cysts are shed in the faeces.

Toxoplasma gondii is an intracellular parasite and actively stimulates macrophages to phagocytose it. Once the organism has been taken up into the macrophage, it prevents the phagocytic vacuole from fusing with lysosomes, and can therefore multiply and persist in the phagocyte. The parasite is able to actively penetrate other types of cells and also forms cysts in the CNS, lungs and muscles (Figure 5.8b). Another way of becoming infected with *T. gondii* is to eat animals that have these cysts in their tissues, which explains why humans can be infected by undercooked meat.

T. gondii infections are common in humans but are mostly asymptomatic, and if symptoms do occur they may be limited to a mild flu-like illness. Acute toxoplasmosis is more unpleasant and can involve painful swelling of the lymph glands and necrosis (tissue death) of the lung, heart and liver.

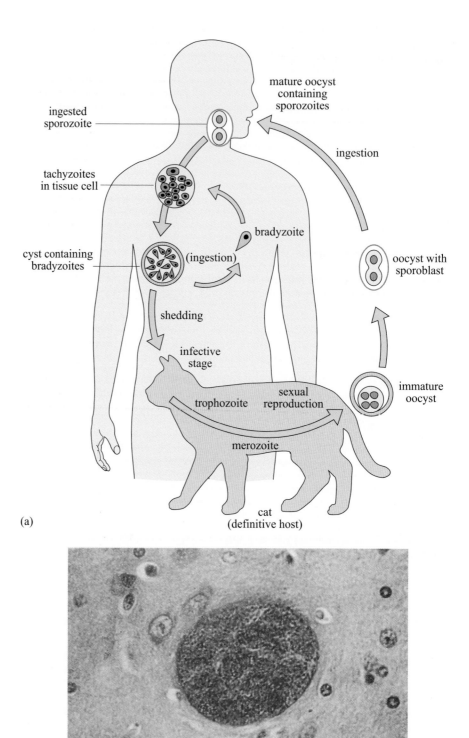

(a)

mature oocyst
containing
sporozoites

ingested
sporozoite

ingestion

tachyzoites
in tissue cell

bradyzoite

oocyst with
sporoblast

cyst containing
bradyzoites

(ingestion)

shedding

infective
stage

immature
oocyst

trophozoite

sexual
reproduction

merozoite

cat
(definitive host)

(b)

20 μm

FIGURE 5.8

(a) Life cycle of *Toxoplasma gondii*. Humans may be infected by oocysts from cats, or by ingestion (in meat) of cysts containing bradyzoites. (b) A cyst of *T. gondii* in mouse brain; hundreds of individuals may be present within the cyst.

Toxoplasmosis has become an important killer of immunosuppressed individuals, such as patients with AIDS, in whom it causes encephalitis. *Toxoplasma gondii* may also establish a persistent infection that can be reactivated to produce neurological disease, but it is best known for its devastating effects on the human fetus. Infection *in utero* can cause congenital abnormalities of the eyes or brain, or even stillbirth. Pregnant women in the UK are made aware of the dangers of toxoplasmosis, and are encouraged to take the appropriate preventative measures. These include washing the hands after time in the garden, cooking all food thoroughly and avoiding exposure to cat faeces in the home or garden.

Toxoplasmosis may be treated with a combination of pyrimethamine and sulfadiazine. In pregnancy, spiramycin may be used and clindamycin has been used to treat infections involving the brain.

5.5.2 Cryptosporidiosis

The protoctists that cause the human diarrhoeal disease known as **cryptosporidiosis** belong to the genus *Cryptosporidium*, and were first recognized as human pathogens in 1976. Since then, they have been identified as the cause of a number of large-scale outbreaks of diarrhoea, but the most well-known of these occurred in Milwaukee, Wisconsin in 1993. Cryptosporidia are often isolated from cattle, and their resistant oocysts (Figure 5.9) are shed in the faeces. In Milwaukee the water supply became contaminated with cattle faeces containing such oocysts, and the water purification system failed to remove them. The infectious oocysts are only 4–6 μm in diameter and are too small to be removed by ordinary filtration. To make matters worse, the oocysts are also resistant to chlorine, and in Milwaukee the result of the contamination episode was 400 000 cases of diarrhoea.

Cryptosporidium parvum, which is frequently found in the intestines of many animals and birds, is the parasite most often associated with cryptosporidiosis. Ingesting only 10–100 of its oocysts in faecally contaminated food or water is enough to cause the infection, and the oocysts are common in sewage, reservoirs and river water. After ingestion, the oocysts excyst in the small intestine, undergo sporogony (spore formation) and release haploid infective organisms called sporozoites.

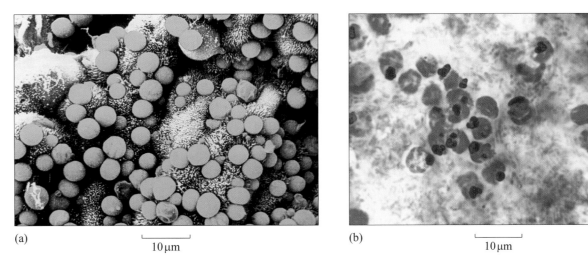

(a)   10 μm   (b)   10 μm

FIGURE 5.9 (a) Scanning electron micrograph of oocysts of *Cryptosporidium parvum* attached to the intestinal epithelium (false colour). (b) *C. parvum* oocysts in faeces; the oocysts are stained pink, while other components of faeces are stained blue.

These sporozoites invade the epithelial cells of the host's intestine and divide to produce merozoites, some of which become gametes and fuse to reproduce sexually. Sexual reproduction results in the formation of the resistant oocysts, which are shed in the faeces to infect other hosts. The life cycle of *Cryptosporidium* is illustrated in Figure 5.10.

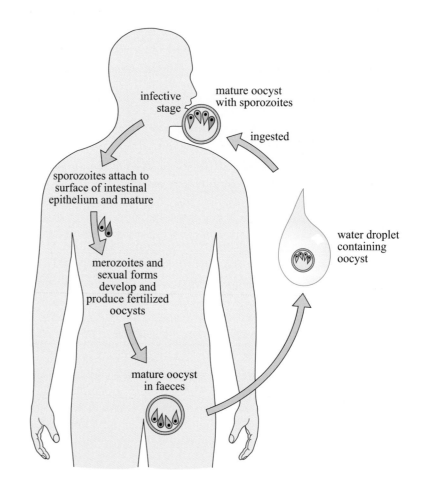

FIGURE 5.10 Life cycle of *Cryptosporidium.*

The symptoms of cryptosporidiosis begin 5–28 days after infection and consist mainly of profuse, watery diarrhoea, although there may be abdominal pain, nausea and fatigue as well. In healthy individuals, the disease is self-limiting, and recovery occurs after several days. In the immunocompromised, it can be far more serious, leading to chronic diarrhoea. In AIDS patients, the presence of chronic, severe cryptosporidial diarrhoea often marks the transition to full-blown AIDS. These patients may also suffer from a rare form of cryptosporidial meningitis. There is no specific treatment for cryptosporidiosis; the patients are usually just rehydrated, but paromomycin can be used if the infection is life-threatening.

Summary of Section 5.5

1   The apicomplexans are all single-celled parasites of animals.

2   Among the diseases they cause are malaria, toxoplasmosis and cryptosporidiosis.

3   Apicomplexans have complex life cycles involving sexual and asexual reproduction.

4   Diseases caused by apicomplexans are particularly serious in immunocompromised individuals.

Learning outcomes for Chapter 5

When you have studied this chapter, you should be able to:

5.1   Define and use, or recognize definitions and applications of, each of the terms printed in **bold** in the text. (*all Section 5 questions*)

5.2   Name some important protoctist pathogens, and describe their life cycles and the diseases they cause. (*Question 5.1*)

5.3   Explain why antiprotoctist drug therapy is of limited success. (*Question 5.2*)

5.4   Outline the importance of clean drinking water in terms of protoctist infection. (*Question 5.3*)

Questions for Chapter 5

Question 5.1

Name the pathogens that give rise to the following diseases, and state what kind of protoctist they are: toxoplasmosis, giardiasis, Chagas' disease, keratitis.

Question 5.2

List the targets of antiprotoctist drugs and state whether these targets are also present in host cells.

Question 5.3

Name three protoctist pathogens that can be transmitted via infected drinking water.

6 THE FUNGI

Fungi are eukaryotic organisms with heterotrophic nutrition (that is, requiring organic material from the environment), existing as **saprophytes** (organisms that obtain organic matter from dead organisms), parasites and commensals. There is useful background material on fungi in the Reference CD (S204 Book 4, Chapter 1). Most fungi are saprophytes and are found in soil, where their saprophytic activity is of great importance in decomposing dead organic matter. As parasites, they are the main cause of plant disease, with over 5000 species of fungus known to be plant pathogens. Commensal fungi gain their nutrition from their host without causing any harm, unless the host becomes compromised in some way, when the fungi can cause endogenous infections. The fungi are split into two main groups: the **moulds**, which grow as a series of interconnected hyphae (see below) with many nuclei in a common cytoplasm; and the **yeasts**, which grow principally as individual cells. Humans have exploited fungi, especially yeasts, since ancient times to make wine, beer and bread. Fungi continue to be important in many industrial processes today, such as the manufacture of cheeses, antibiotics and other drugs. Here we look at the very few species that are human pathogens.

6.1 Fungal structure and reproduction

Morphologically, fungi vary enormously, from microscopic single-celled yeasts and multicellular moulds to macroscopic structures such as toadstools (Figure 6.1). Despite this diversity, fungi share a number of basic characteristics. There is usually a well-defined, rigid cell wall composed of about 80% polysaccharide, 10% protein and 10% lipid. **Chitin**, a polymer of *N*-acetylglucosamine, is one of the most important of these structural polysaccharides.

○ Where else have you encountered the complex monosaccharide *N*-acetylglucosamine?

● Along with *N*-acetylmuramic acid, it makes up the basic structure of peptidoglycan, a major structural component of bacterial cell walls.

Interestingly, chitin is also found in the exoskeletons of insects. Other polysaccharides found in fungal cell walls include glucans (polymers of glucose) and mannans (polymers of the sugar mannose) but the exact cell-wall composition varies depending on the particular fungus. In addition to the cell wall, fungi have a plasma membrane, containing characteristic sterols such as **ergosterol**, and many of the membrane-bound organelles found in other eukaryotic cells.

Moulds grow by extension of branched cellular filaments called **hyphae**, which may have cross-walls or septa (singular: septum), or form one continuous tube. If cross-walls are present, they are perforated, allowing continuity of the cytoplasm throughout the hypha. Hyphae grow by apical extension and form thick networks called **mycelia** (singular: mycelium). As a result of their structure and growth pattern, moulds are also known as filamentous or mycelial fungi. Moulds reproduce by means of spores, which can be formed by either asexual cell division or sexual reproduction.

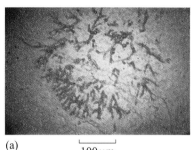
(a) 100 µm

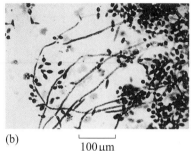
(b) 100 µm

(c) 3 cm

FIGURE 6.1
Fungal morphology. (a) Hyphae of *Aspergillus fumigatus* in a skin specimen. (b) Sputum sample containing yeast and hyphal forms of *Candida*. (c) *Amanita*, a poisonous toadstool.

Yeasts are single-celled fungi, round or oval in shape, and typically larger than bacterial cells, measuring 6–8 μm in diameter. They reproduce by asexual budding, where a cell develops a protuberance that grows larger and, with its own nucleus, finally separates from the parent cell. A few yeasts reproduce by a fission process. Some fungi, called **dimorphic fungi**, are able to grow as either moulds or yeasts depending on the growth conditions. Many human pathogens are dimorphic, for example *Candida albicans*, the agent that causes thrush.

Summary of Section 6.1

1   Fungi generally grow as filamentous hyphae or single-celled yeasts, although some are dimorphic.

2   The fungal cell wall is composed largely of chitin, a polymer of *N*-acetyl-glucosamine.

3   The fungal plasma membrane contains ergosterol.

4   Fungi reproduce by forming sexual and asexual spores.

5   Filamentous fungi grow by hyphal extension; yeasts can replicate by fission or budding.

6.2 Fungal nutrition

There are a number of different modes of fungal nutrition, but most fungi are saprophytes. Some saprophytic fungi change their mode of nutrition to **biotrophy** (obtaining organic matter from living organisms) once inside the host. Whatever their mode of nutrition, all fungi release enzymes outside the cell to digest external substrates, and then absorb the soluble products.

◯   Suggest what the effect of these enzymes on the host's tissue might be.

⬤   Enzyme activity would cause local tissue degradation and the release of cellular contents. This causes tissue damage to the host and has important consequences for the immune response, as you will see in Book 3.

The diseases caused by fungi are called **mycoses**.

Summary of Section 6.2

1   Mycoses are caused by biotrophic fungi.

2   Enzymes released by the fungus cause tissue damage to the host.

6.3 Fungi and infectious disease in humans and other animals

Of the many thousands of species of fungi which have been described, only about 180 of them are known to cause disease in animals. Fewer still, around 50 species, are human pathogens. Most mycoses are not life-threatening, but can still cause much suffering and disfigurement. However, opportunistic fungal infections, which are more frequently life-threatening, are becoming increasingly important. These infections occur in individuals whose resistance to infection is reduced in some way, such as by disease or drug therapy. Opportunistic mycoses are important infections in AIDS patients, and are a leading cause of death in transplant recipients. The fungi responsible usually have an endogenous or environmental origin, so these diseases are not regarded as infectious.

Mycoses are classified according to the location of the infection, as **superficial**, **subcutaneous** or **systemic**. Superficial infections are found on the hair, skin, nails and mucous membranes. Subcutaneous mycoses are caused by soil fungi, which gain access to the body through puncture wounds, but are unable to breach intact skin. Systemic mycoses spread throughout the body and are mostly acquired by inhaling fungal spores produced by soil fungi. Subcutaneous and systemic mycoses are usually acquired from the environment, whereas superficial mycoses are contracted by person-to-person contact.

☐ Which of these types of mycosis is infectious?

⬛ The superficial mycoses are the only class of mycosis to be truly infectious, as only they are transmitted from person to person.

Mycoses are known to provoke immune responses, but the details of such responses are not well understood.

6.3.1 Superficial mycoses

Mycoses of the skin, hair, nails and mucous membranes are the commonest type of fungal infection and have a worldwide distribution. These diseases are mainly caused by ringworm fungi and yeasts. We will look at them in turn.

Ringworm

Ringworm fungi are a group of around 20 closely related mould fungi from three genera: *Trichophyton*, *Microsporum* and *Epidermophyton*. These are known collectively as **dermatophytes** and can digest keratin, a tough fibrous protein found in the skin, hair and nails. Ringworm infections are often called **tineas** (Figure 6.2 overleaf explains why) and are specifically related to their location, e.g. tinea capitis is ringworm of the scalp and tinea pedis is ringworm of the foot. (Note that tinea capitis and tinea pedis are *not* the names of particular species.) Some dermatophytes that are primarily animal pathogens can also infect humans. Bovine ringworm is highly infectious for people in contact with infected cattle.

Ringworm infection is introduced to the host via a keratin fragment containing the fungus. This can be the result of direct contact or via fomites such as swimming pool floors and the floors of communal showers or baths. Shared brushes, combs, towels or grooming equipment in animals can all be sources of infection. The fungus can remain viable for long periods of time between leaving one host and arriving on another. It is thought that the skin needs to have been damaged by minor trauma before a ringworm infection can become established. The lesions produced by ringworm vary according to the site infected and the pathogen responsible (see Figure 6.2). There may just be dry scaling or an excessive production of keratin (hyperkeratosis), but usually the symptoms are more marked. Infection with dermatophytes that are primarily animal pathogens results in more severe lesions with blisters, pustules (pimples containing pus) and ulceration.

Tinea pedis, or athlete's foot as it is more commonly known, is a dermatophyte infection mostly caused by *Trichophyton rubrum*, *T. mentagrophytes* or *Epidermophyton floccosum*. Tinea pedis has a worldwide distribution and is most common in adults, especially males. The infection can be limited to the toe clefts, or it may spread to the sole. Itching is common and skin lesions are circular with a raised inflammatory border. The toenails are frequently involved and become raised, thickened, discoloured and brittle. The likelihood of infection is increased by occlusion (covering), warmth and moisture. Such conditions are readily provided for the feet when shoes are worn. Ringworm of the groin and hands often follows infection of the feet. Foot ringworm and associated infections now represent 75% of all ringworm infections diagnosed in temperate climates.

Tinea capitis is a dermatophyte infection of the scalp hair, found most commonly in children, and mainly caused by *Trichophyton* or *Microsporum* species. Scalp infections, together with body (tinea corporis) and groin (tinea cruris) ringworm are especially prevalent in developing countries, particularly those with a warm climate. Conversely, in developed countries tinea capitis is responsible for only a small proportion of ringworm infections, and these are mainly contracted from animals. Scalp ringworm causes inflammation and scaling of the scalp, and hair loss. In males, the beard may also be involved. Dermatophytes caught from animals can produce a kerion, which is a raised, suppurating lesion. If scalp ringworm is not treated quickly, it can lead to scarring and permanent hair loss. Person-to-person transmission of ringworm occurs most easily where there is overcrowding and poor hygiene.

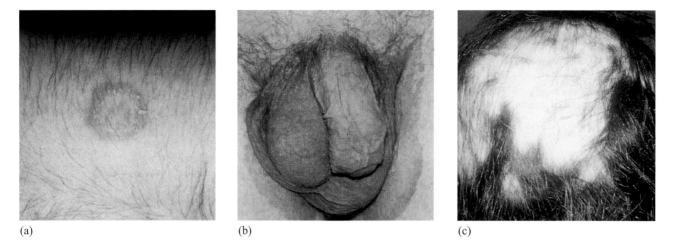

(a)　　　　　　　　　　(b)　　　　　　　　　　(c)

FIGURE 6.2 Appearance of various tineas: (a) tinea corporis, caused by a *Microsporum* species; (b) tinea cruris; (c) tinea capitis. (The word 'tinea' derives from the similarity of the rounded lesions seen on the skin of many patients to the circular holes in fabrics caused by the larvae of moths of the genus *Tinea*.)

Ringworm may be diagnosed from samples of infected skin, hair and nail by microscopical examination and subsequent culture of the fungus. Topical (locally applied) antifungal drugs are sufficient for most infections, but oral therapy is needed to treat infections involving the nails and scalp, and for severe skin infections. Little has been done to prevent ringworm infections. The incidence of scalp ringworm has been reduced by improved diagnosis of the infection and better standards of living, rather than by active prevention. Footbaths at swimming pools, which are designed to prevent the spread of infectious disease including athlete's foot, are of no use against dermatophyte infections.

◻ Why is this the case?

▣ Footbaths just concentrate infected material in a place where most people walk.

Fortunately, the use of antifungal foot powder after bathing is effective at preventing ringworm infections.

Superficial candidosis

These infections are caused by dimorphic yeasts that belong to the genus *Candida*. About 20% of the population harbour *Candida* yeasts, usually *C. albicans*, as commensals on the skin, and in the mouth, gastrointestinal tract and vagina. Superficial candidoses of the mouth and vagina, known as thrush infections, are the result of an overgrowth of these endogenous yeasts. Overgrowth is a result of the host becoming compromised in some way, such as by pregnancy, antibiotic treatment or immunosuppression. Thrush infections are therefore endogenous in nature and are rarely an infectious disease. However, thrush can be transmitted from person to person during sexual intercourse, resulting in an inflammation of the glans penis known as balanitis. *Candida* infection may also be acquired by a baby during birth, from the mother, if she has a vaginal thrush infection.

6.3.2 Subcutaneous and systemic mycoses

Subcutaneous mycoses are most often contracted by agricultural workers in tropical and subtropical climates, who work barefoot. The diseases most often involve the legs and feet and develop slowly, producing ulcerating nodules.

Most systemic mycoses are caused by dimorphic fungi and are contracted by inhaling fungal spores. Fungal spores are always present in the air, but are more numerous when the earth has been disturbed. For this reason, the systemic mycoses are most common in farm workers and builders. If enough spores are taken into the lung, a focus (plural: foci) of infection can develop from which the fungus can disseminate further. Disseminated fungal infections are the most serious type of mycosis, and have an especially poor prognosis in patients with compromised immunity.

Summary of Section 6.3

1   Mycoses can be superficial, subcutaneous or systemic. Only superficial mycoses are truly infectious.

2   Ringworm infections, caused by dermatophytes, commonly affect the scalp or the feet, and have a worldwide distribution.

3   Thrush is caused by *Candida* yeasts, and is very common throughout the world.

4   Subcutaneous mycoses occur most often in people who work barefoot.

5   Systemic mycoses can result in disseminated infections, which are serious diseases, especially in immunocompromised people.

Learning outcomes for Chapter 6

When you have studied this chapter, you should be able to:

6.1   Define and use, or recognize definitions and applications of, each of the terms printed in **bold** in the text. (*Questions 6.1 and 6.2*)

6.2   Outline how fungal nutrition can cause disease. (*Question 6.2*)

6.3   Use named examples to describe the aetiology of common mycoses. (*Questions 6.1 and 6.2*)

Questions for Chapter 6

Question 6.1

A farm worker goes to the GP with a mycosis on his foot. Suggest three possible routes by which he could have acquired this infection.

Question 6.2

How does *Candida* cause balanitis?

7 PARASITIC INVERTEBRATES

If you are interested in learning more about the main taxonomic classes of parasitic invertebrates, and, in general terms, their life cycles, this material is covered in the Reference CD (S204 Book 6, Chapter 3).

7.1 Introduction

We turn now from a study of single-celled protoctistan parasites to examine the effect of multicellular invertebrate parasites. Although we concentrate on some of those parasites that cause debilitating diseases in humans, it is important to recognize the ubiquitous nature of invertebrate parasites, since it has been suggested that over 50% of all individual animals and plants are infected, at least at some stage of their life cycle. Parasites occur as members of virtually all invertebrate groups, and although some may have devastating effects on their hosts, many hosts tolerate a parasite burden with little obvious effect.

Some of the more important parasitic infections of humans are caused by various worms known generally as **helminths**. These include the majority of animal parasites found living on or within vertebrates and are represented in two phyla: the Platyhelminthes (flatworms) and the Nematoda (roundworms). Although these groups incorporate the 'parasitic worms', in fact many parasites are worm-like (recall from Section 5.3, and the Malaria Case Study, the shape of the invasive stages of the protoctists *Trypanosoma* and *Plasmodium*).

○ Why do you think that parasites have evolved this morphological characteristic?

● Such a shape is useful for taking up residence in tubular cavities of hosts, such as the gut and blood vessels, and would also favour penetration into or through host tissue.

Table 7.1 (overleaf) shows the estimated occurrence of some important helminth parasites of humans and their distribution throughout the world.

○ What do you notice about the worldwide distribution of these parasites?

● A large number occur in tropical or subtropical areas.

○ Can you think of reasons for this?

● Environmental conditions may favour the continuation of the parasite's life cycle in these areas. Also the helminths tend to be mainly in developing countries where poverty, resulting in unhygienic conditions of contaminated soil and water, may favour the survival of parasite stages.

TABLE 7.1 Estimate of current human infection by some helminth parasites.

Phylum	Parasite	Location in host	Disease	Numbers infected (millions)	Distribution
Platyhelminthes (flukes)	Schistosoma spp.	blood vessels (around gut or bladder)	schistosomiasis (bilharzia)	200	Africa, Asia
	Clonorchis sinensis	bile duct, gall bladder, liver	clonorchiasis	30	Far East
	Fasciolopsis buski	intestine	fascioliasis	10	Eastern Asia, Southwest Pacific countries
	Paragonimus westermani	lungs	paragonomiasis	20	worldwide
Platyhelminthes (tapeworms)	Taenia solium	adult in gut larval cysts may infect other tissues, e.g. brain	taeniasis cysticercosis	10	worldwide
	Echinococcus granulosus	cysts in brain, liver, lungs	hydatidosis	2.7	worldwide
	Diphyllobothrium latum	intestine	diphyllobothriasis	9	northern USA, Canada, Scandinavia, Balkans, Far East
Nematoda (roundworms)	Ancylostoma spp.	intestine	ancylostomiasis	} 1298	southern Europe, Africa, Far East, southern USA, South America
	Necator spp.	intestine	necatoriasis		
	Ascaris sp.	intestine	ascariasis	1472	worldwide
	Anisakis simplex	larva penetrates through intestine wall	anisakiasis	up to 0.1	North Atlantic countries
	Brugia sp., Wucheraria sp.	lymphatic system	filariasis	120	Asia, Southwest Pacific countries
	Onchocerca volvulus	eye	river blindness (onchocerciasis)	18	central South America, Sub-Saharan Africa
	Dracunculus medinensis	under skin	dracunculiasis	3–4	Sub-Saharan Africa, Sudan, Southeast Asia

Before dealing with the pathobiological effects of helminth parasites and the subsequent costs in terms of human misery, we need to examine how the life cycles of flukes, tapeworms and roundworms are beautifully adapted to enhancing transmission from one host to another.

7.2 Parasite transfer from host to host

The introduction to this book outlined the various mechanisms by which parasites, microbes especially, are transferred from host to host.

◻ Recall how such transmission was generally described.

⬤ Horizontal transmission (person-to-person spread) and vertical transmission (from parent to offspring *in utero*, etc.).

Parasitic helminths are transmitted horizontally. Flukes (including all those that are human parasites), tapeworms and roundworms have elaborate and complicated transfer mechanisms compared with microbes.

◻ Why do you think that adult macroparasites need different transmission strategies compared with microbes?

⬤ They are too large (see Table 1.1) to become airborne or to penetrate by direct contact into a host, even if they could be transferred directly, e.g. by water.

Thus, most of these parasites have evolved special morphological and physiological adaptations, involving the production of large numbers of eggs and a variety of complex larval stages which enhance survival and transfer between hosts. In addition, many of the pathobiological effects on the host may be part of an adaptive mechanism to change host behaviour in favour of transfer of the parasite to another host.

To appreciate first of all some of the fascinating, if sometimes bizarre, ways in which parasites ensure their transfer, examine Figure 7.1 overleaf.

◻ List the main features that you consider to be similar in the three life cycle strategies, and those that you consider to be different.

⬤ *Similarities*:
  1 Adult parasites exhibit sexual reproduction.
  2 Eggs may be released into water.
  3 Larval stages are involved in transfer between hosts.
  4 Larval stages usually enter the **definitive** (i.e. final) host in food (although penetration by larvae may occur in some flukes and roundworms).

  Differences:
  1 In flukes and tapeworms, **intermediate hosts** are always involved in the life cycle. Roundworm larvae do not usually use an intermediate host although, in a few groups, a **vector** is involved. The vector usually effects transfer actively, e.g. by biting, whereas if the larval stages are free-living, transfer to the human host is passive, e.g. by being eaten.
  2 Asexual reproductive stages occur in all flukes and some tapeworms but only sexual reproduction occurs in roundworms.

When an intermediate host or a vector is involved, the life cycle is said to be **indirect**. In all other cases the life cycle is **direct**.

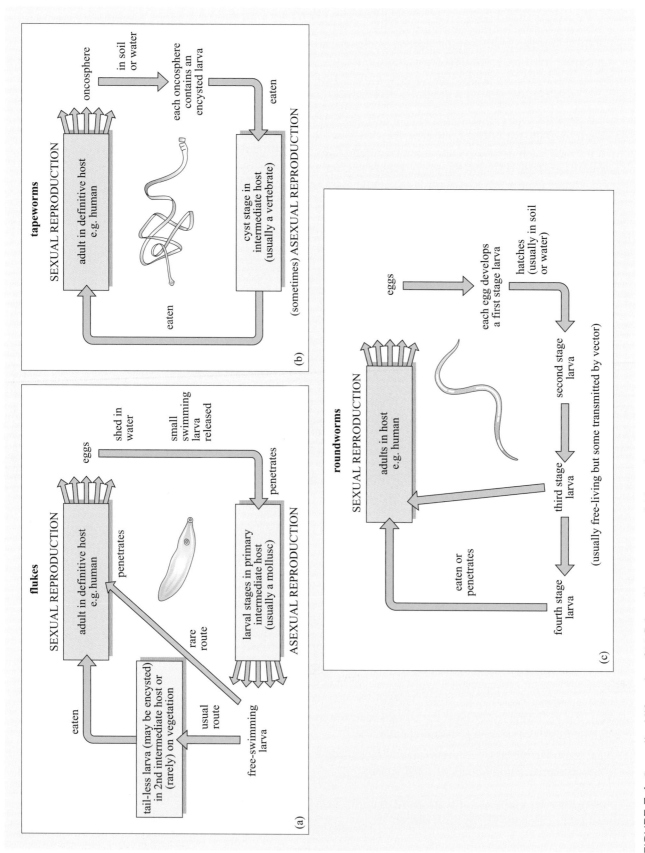

FIGURE 7.1   Generalized life cycles of (a) flukes, (b) tapeworms and (c) roundworms.

The chance of one single offspring of an adult parasite finding another host before it dies is exceedingly small. To compensate for such mortality, parasites produce very large numbers of offspring at certain stages of their life cycle. Hundreds, sometimes thousands, of eggs are released after each mating by the adults. Roundworms usually, but not always, have separate sexes, but flukes and tapeworms almost always show hermaphroditism, although cross-fertilization is the norm.

In flukes, the many small swimming larvae, just a few micrometres in size, are released from the egg. Each is called a miracidium (Figure 7.2a) and they frantically search for a specific mollusc (usually a snail) to which they are chemically attracted, before their energy supply is exhausted. If successful, they penetrate into the soft tissues of the mollusc, where they develop into a sac-like sporocyst larva (Figure 7.2b). Each sporocyst develops more sporocysts and within each of these sporocysts, many individuals of a third type of larva may develop asexually. These are called redia larvae. Each redia larva (or sporocyst if no redia larva is produced)

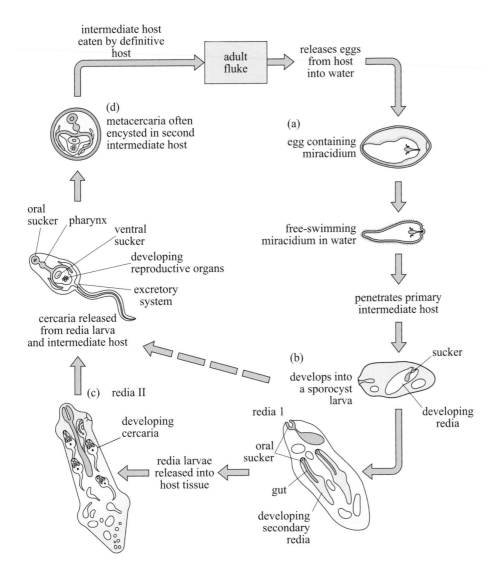

FIGURE 7.2
Diagrammatic representation of larval stages of flukes (not to scale).

produces asexually hundreds of cercaria larvae (Figure 7.2c), which are shed from the mollusc. These are sperm-like in appearance and swim by lashing their tails. If they find a specific second intermediate host, they penetrate into it, lose the tail, and encyst, where they are known as a metacercaria larva (Figure 7.2d), the fifth larval type of this strange life cycle.

If the intermediate host is eaten by its predator, which is the definitive host, the metacercaria excysts and develops into an adult fluke.

In tapeworms, a hooked larva known as a hexacanth develops inside the egg, or oncosphere (Figure 7.3a). If the oncosphere is taken in by the correct intermediate host, the hexacanth is released in the gut, penetrates into the tissues, and forms a cyst stage, the cysticercus, which contains a small invaginated (turned inside out) tapeworm head (Figure 7.3b). If this intermediate host is eaten by the definitive host, the tapeworm head evaginates (pops out) and attaches to the gut wall. Many segments are produced behind the head region (some tapes can reach several metres in length!) and each individual segment, after sexual reproduction, can produce hundreds of eggs or oncospheres. In some species of tapeworm, the cysticercus stage exhibits massive asexual reproduction and buds many cysts within cysts (rather like a Russian doll), so that from one invading hexacanth, hundreds, even thousands, of tapeworm heads (scoleces) develop. These cysts are called hydatid cysts (Figure 7.3c).

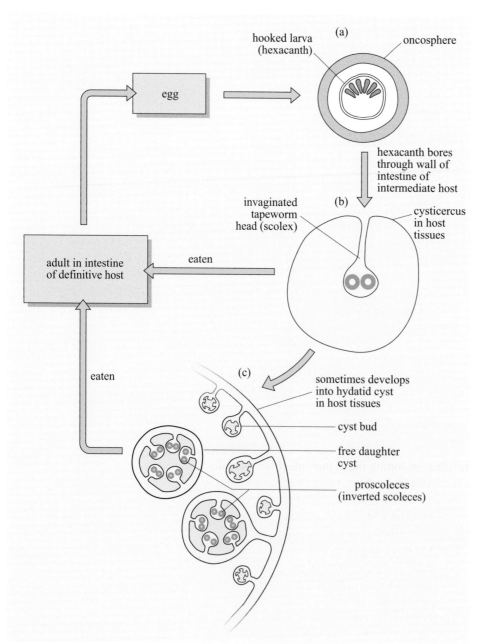

FIGURE 7.3
Diagrammatic representation of larval stages of tapeworms (not to scale).

By comparison with flukes and tapeworms, roundworm life cycles are much more straightforward (Figure 7.4).

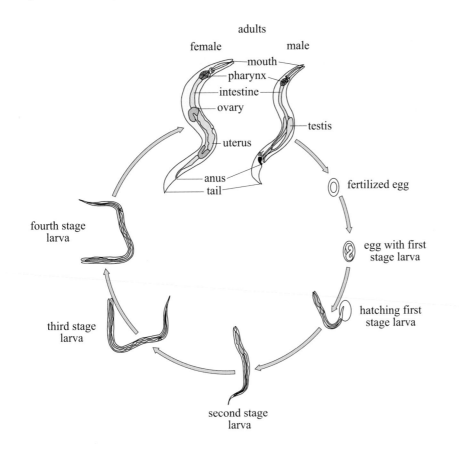

FIGURE 7.4
Generalized representation of roundworm larval stages (not to scale).

Although many eggs are produced by the adult roundworm, there are two important adaptive features that explain why roundworms have not evolved asexual stages. Firstly, the eggs are extremely resistant and can survive in the environment for a considerable length of time. For example, the eggs of the dog roundworm, *Toxocara canis*, can remain viable in soils in parks and children's playgrounds for a number of years. If accidentally ingested by a child, the egg hatches and the larva migrates to various body tissues. It has been known occasionally to lodge behind the eye where it has encysted and caused a tumour to develop. Secondly, roundworms, including their larvae, have a thick cuticle which again assists survival until a new host may be found.

With a few exceptions, most adult parasites, including those that infect humans, do not kill their hosts. However, there is accumulating evidence that the parasite can affect the behaviour, especially of intermediate hosts, to enforce transmission. *Dicrocoelium dendriticum,* for example, is a liver fluke found in cattle worldwide. Its second intermediate host is an ant into which the cercariae penetrate. Within the ant, metacercarial cysts normally occur in the body cavity, but at least one cercaria migrates to, and encysts in, the brain of the ant. There it interferes with the neural pathway that controls jaw function, which normally operates as temperature falls, to open the jaw and so allow the ant to cease feeding and retreat into the soil. The result of neural disruption by the encysted cercaria is that the ant remains firmly clamped by its mouth onto a blade of grass, just at a time when cattle graze extensively, thus ensuring transfer of the metacercaria stage to the definitive host (Curio, 1988).

In terms of human parasites, a sound knowledge of the life cycle of the parasite and any behavioural aberrations of hosts is essential for the employment of effective methods of prevention and control. Some 287 helminth species have been reported in humans (Taylor *et al.*, 2001), of which significant disease is caused by 25 fluke species, 14 tapeworms, and 36 roundworms (Mata, 1982). We turn our attention now to examine a few of these pathogenic helminths in more detail.

7.3 Fluke diseases

7.3.1 Blood flukes

By any standard, the most important human fluke disease is **schistosomiasis**, which is caused by infection by blood flukes of a number of species of *Schistosoma* (schistosomes). The disease was originally known as bilharzia, worms having been first discovered at autopsy in a Cairo hospital by the German surgeon Theodor Bilharz in 1851 (Figure 7.5). However, the disease was certainly known many centuries before this, as it is possible that hieroglyphics (Figure 7.6) from around 1500 BC depict a disease which was described in medical papyri from those times as âaâ – this was thought to mean 'haematuria' (urinary bleeding), which is depicted by the bottom-right symbol in the hieroglyphic. One species, *Schistosoma haematobium*, is found in the blood vessels around the bladder and causes this symptom. Subsequently, calcified eggs of blood flukes have been found in mummies and, with molecular techniques, schistosome antigens have been detected in a mummy from 3200 BC! (Miller *et al.*, 1992).

FIGURE 7.5
Theodor Bilharz (1825–1862).

FIGURE 7.6
Representation of a section of Egyptian hieroglyphic from the Ebers papyrus written in 1500 BC.

Urinary schistosomiasis, caused by *S. haematobium*, is particularly prevalent in the Nile Delta but is also found, along with *Schistosoma mansoni* – which occurs in the veins around the gut, causing intestinal schistosomiasis – in large areas of Sub-Saharan Africa (Figure 7.7). *S. mansoni* also occurs along the eastern part of central South America, and another intestinal species, *Schistosoma japonicum*, is restricted to the Far East (Figure 7.7).

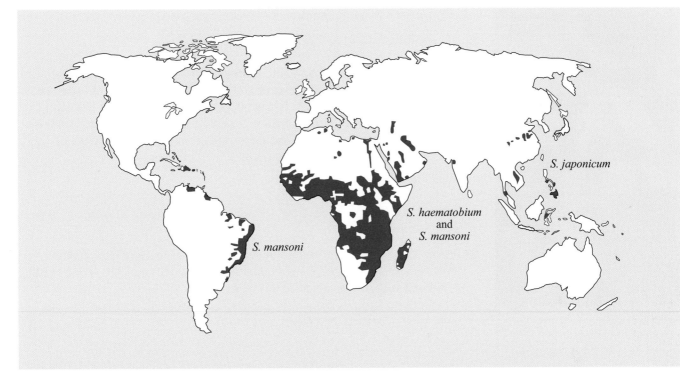

FIGURE 7.7 Global distribution of the three major species of *Schistosoma* that cause the disease schistosomiasis.

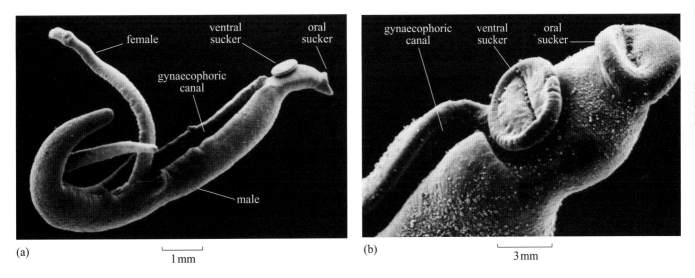

FIGURE 7.8 (a) Scanning electron micrograph of a pair of adult *Schistosoma mansoni* worms. (b) Scanning electron micrograph of *S. mansoni*, showing a close-up of the oral and ventral suckers and the gynaecophoric canal.

Thus, depending on species, adult schistosomes (Figure 7.8) are found in the blood vessels of the intestine, and sometimes in the liver and bladder. As in all flukes, a complicated life cycle ensures that eggs released from one definitive host have a good chance of becoming established as adult worms in another host. Look again at Figures 7.1a and 7.2.

FIGURE 7.9
Recreational transmission of
schistosomes – children playing in
a snail infested irrigation system.

○ What are the three requirements of the schistosome life cycle?

● Human hosts, water and molluscs.

In many parts of the developing world, especially in the rural areas, safe clean water and good sanitation procedures are often lacking. Such areas of water that there are become used intensively by members of the community for bathing (Figure 7.9), washing and crop irrigation. It is not hard to imagine that such water becomes contaminated with urine and faeces and, should any of the users be harbouring blood flukes, eggs will be released into the water.

Examine Figure 7.10.

○ What conclusions can you draw concerning the prevalence of infection in these communities?

● 1 Prevalence appears to be closely related to the distance of each community from the nearest infected water – although it rises betwwen 410 m and 600 m, it falls off with distance outside this range.

2 As *S. haematobium* infection is more prevalent than *S. mansoni* infection, urine contamination of infected water is more likely than faecal contamination.

○ From your knowledge of the generalized life cycle of flukes (Figures 7.1a and 7.2), how is the snail intermediate host involved?

● Eggs hatch to release a free-swimming miracidium larva. This larva encounters a snail (probably by chemoattraction), penetrates the tissue and develops into a first stage (mother) sporocyst larva.

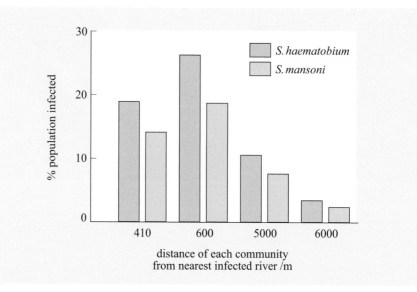

FIGURE 7.10 Relationship between prevalence of blood fluke infection and distance (in metres) from infected water in Bauchi State, Nigeria.

Unlike many flukes, no redia stage is produced, but prolific asexual reproduction results in further (daughter) sporocysts and many thousands of cercariae, which are released into the water. As each snail is probably infected by many miracidia, hundreds of thousands of cercariae may be released periodically into these watercourses.

Cercariae swim by means of powerful tails (Figure 7.11) and, unlike most flukes, do not enter another host to encyst as metacercariae, but penetrate directly through the skin of a human host. Within the host, the tail is lost and each schistosome, now known as a schistosomula, follows a long route through the lymphatic and blood systems, via the lungs, eventually ending up in the liver. Unlike most other flukes, schistosomes are unisexual, and in the liver each male and female worm pairs up, the male holding the more slender female in a special ventral, gynaecophoric canal (Figure 7.8). They then migrate to the blood vessels around the intestine or bladder, depending on species.

Adult worms may live for several years and, as there may be a number of pairs in the blood vessels, many thousands of eggs are produced.

Figure 7.12 shows the prevalence of infection across an age range of infected Nigerian individuals.

○ What do the data suggest regarding infection of children and adults?

● 1 Children are not immune to infection and probably become infected when old enough to play in infected water (the peak of infection is in the early teens).

2 The decline in prevalence of infection with age during adulthood is probably due to reduction in contact with water associated with changed leisure and work patterns.

3 The lower egg output in older groups of individuals suggests that adults may have acquired immunity to infection.

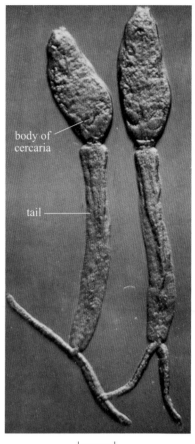

body of cercaria

tail

0.1 mm

FIGURE 7.11
Cercariae of *Schistosoma mansoni*.

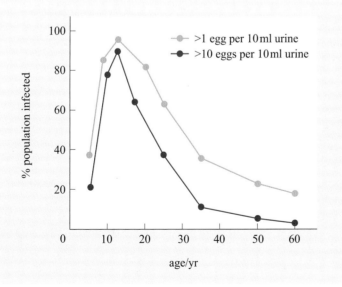

FIGURE 7.12
Relationship between prevalence of *Schistosoma haematobium* infection and age in Bauchi State, Nigeria.

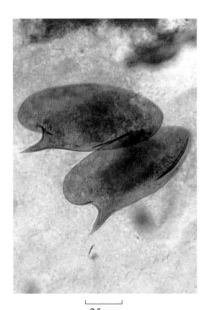

25 μm

FIGURE 7.13
Eggs of *Schistosoma mansoni* showing the sharp lateral spines.

A considerable amount of research has been undertaken concerning immunity to schistosomiasis, and is summarized by Rollinson and Johnston (1996). Human hosts appear to be able to resist further infections, even though adult worms survive in their blood vessels. This is known as **concomitant immunity**, where the immune response acts against new invading cercariae. Why is it that the adult worms are not challenged successfully by the immune system? The answer lies in the fact that worms may adopt a disguise by coating themselves with host macromolecules. More recent work has suggested that some worms may be able to suppress their own antigens or even release substances that may inhibit or, at least, suppress their host's immune response (see Section 1.3).

Why is schistosomiasis such a ravaging disease? The main pathological effects occur because of the way in which eggs are released. The majority of them tear through the intestinal wall (or bladder wall) by means of sharp spines (Figure 7.13). Eggs lodged in the gut wall can cause abscesses, but eggs can end up in a number of body locations, including the lungs, brain, liver and spleen, often causing a huge increase in size of the latter two organs (Figure 7.14). As eggs become lodged in these tissues, they are attacked by the host immune cells, followed by encapsulation and inflammation, resulting in severe disease symptoms. Such symptoms may occur years after the initial infection, are extremely debilitating, and occasionally cause death. Associations between schistosomiasis and the occurrence of some cancers have been identified.

Next to malaria, schistosomiasis is the world's most debilitating parasitic tropical disease and consequently a good deal of effort has gone into methods of its control and prevention.

☐ Consider the schistosome life cycle and suggest four key places where control could be effective.

◼ 1 By preventing contamination of water by eggs, by providing proper sanitation and clean water.

 2 By eliminating the snail host (although in practice this is virtually impossible, given the limited chemical available to kill molluscs).

 3 By preventing humans entering water where infected snails have been identified.

 4 By the administration of chemotherapeutic drugs to infected individuals. (The drug prazaquantel is the most effective, as it can reduce egg output considerably, even though it does not kill the adult worms.)

Very little success has been achieved in the production of a conventional vaccine. However, schistosome genome analysis, coupled with modern molecular techniques, has enabled the cloning of schistosome genes in bacteria or yeast cells, which then express schistosome proteins. Thus, some kind of recombinant vaccine is the great hope for the future (Rollinson and Johnston, 1999).

In the 150 years or so since these fascinating, if dangerous, parasites have been known, much has been revealed about their life cycles, epidemiology and pathobiology, yet they still remain a scourge of their human host. The challenge for future parasitologists is to convert growing molecular understanding into effective prevention measures.

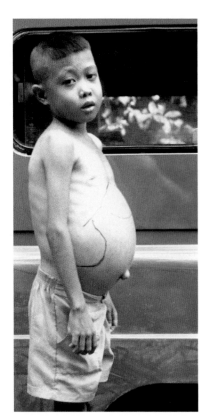

FIGURE 7.14
A Filipino child with enlarged body organs and an umbilical hernia caused by *Schistosoma japonicum* infection.

7.3.2 Other flukes

Although around a dozen other flukes occur in humans, only a few affect large numbers: one such is *Clonorchis sinensis*, the Chinese or Oriental liver-fluke. Adult flukes occur in the bile duct (in the liver), feeding on blood, where they can survive for around 25 years. The life cycle is identical to that represented in Figures 7.1a and 7.2, and when cercariae are released from a freshwater snail (the primary intermediate host), they penetrate into fish such as carp or minnow (the second intermediate host), where they encyst as metacercariae. In the Far East, especially China and Thailand, undercooked, salted, pickled or smoked freshwater fish is considered a delicacy. But such culinary habits often come with a price, as infection by a few flukes can cause serious liver malfunction and, in cases of heavy infection, even death. In many areas, the life cycle is maintained as cats and dogs can be infected and thus act as reservoir hosts.

Other liver-flukes, belonging to the genus *Fasciolopsis,* are large flukes (up to 7 cm in length) occupying the bile duct. Sporocysts, rediae and cercariae occur in freshwater snails but, on release, the cercariae attach to vegetation such as water chestnut. They encyst, and the cyst releases its metacercaria in the intestine of the definitive host when the vegetable is eaten uncooked. The metacercariae then migrate to the bile duct, where they mature. *Fasciolopsis* is common in Eastern Asia and the Southwest Pacific, where it causes profuse diarrhoea, duodenal blockage, generalized toxaemia and sometimes death.

○ What is the main difference between this life cycle and that of *Clonorchis*?

● No intermediate host is involved for the metacercaria stage in the *Fasciolopsis* life cycle, whereas *Clonorchis* uses snails and fish as intermediate hosts.

A closely related fluke, *Fasciola hepatica* (Figure 7.15), is a common liver-fluke of sheep in southwest Britain. The metacercaria often encysts on water-cress leaves and every year a number of localized infections of humans occur as a result of eating wild, and insufficiently washed, water-cress.

Finally, the fluke *Paragonimus westermani* occurs as an adult in the lungs of mammals, in many parts of the world. It is found as a parasite in humans in those areas where there is high consumption of salted, but uncooked crabs.

○ What part in the life cycle do you suspect the crab might play?

● It is the second intermediate host, containing the metacercaria larva which would have reached there from the primary (snail) host.

The metacercaria is often in cysts in the crab and a common route of infection occurs when crabs are 'dressed' on a surface: cysts are released and contaminate salad vegetables also being prepared, that are then eaten uncooked. Paragonomiasis is a dangerous disease. Within the lungs, cysts and adhesions occur, resulting in long-lasting chronic pulmonary problems. Cysts sometimes end up in other tissues, including the brain, causing epilepsy and meningitis.

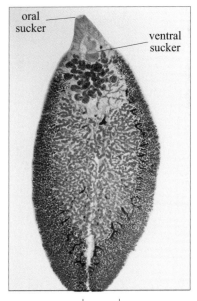

oral sucker

ventral sucker

5 mm

FIGURE 7.15
An adult liver-fluke (*Fasciola hepatica*).

7.4 Tapeworms

Amongst helminth parasites, tapeworms are perhaps the least pathogenic to humans, and they may occur in Western countries as well as developing countries. Generally, they occur attached between gut villi in the intestine, taking up digested food through a specialized body wall, very much in competition with the host's intestinal cells. Indeed, in late Victorian times it was considered fashionable to harbour a tapeworm as an aid to slimming! *Taenia solium* (pork tapeworm) and *Taenia saginata* (beef tapeworm) both fall into this category. In these cases, humans are infected by eating undercooked pork or beef in which the cysticercus larva (Figure 7.3b) has developed.

○ How would swine and cattle have come to harbour the cysticercus stage?

● By picking up oncospheres shed in human faeces and perhaps spread on pasture as fertilizer (see Figure 7.1b and Figure 7.3).

The cysticercus ruptures in the intestine and the small tapeworm head (scolex) evaginates and anchors itself by means of hooks and suckers in the case of *T. solium* (Figure 7.16a), or by suckers in *T. saginata*, between the gut villi. The tapeworm then buds many proglottids (segments) containing the reproductive system (Figure 7.16b).

A more serious aspect of *T. solium* infection for humans is when oncospheres, normally destined for another intermediate host, are taken in accidentally by humans from contaminated faeces. In this case, the hexacanth (hooked larva) can bore

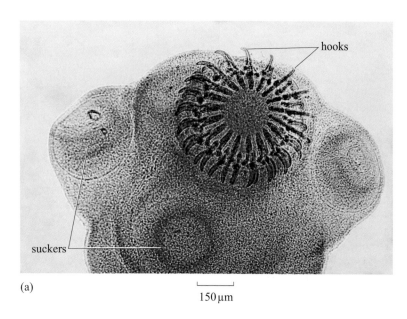

proglottids, each with mature reproductive system

hooks

suckers

(a)

150 µm

(b)

2.5 mm

FIGURE 7.16 (a) Scolex of *Taenia solium* showing hooks and suckers for attachment to gut wall. (b) Mature proglottids of *Taenia* sp., showing the reproductive system, which produces both male and female gametes.

through the tissues to end up in many different organs as a cysticercus (as shown earlier in Figure 7.3). In the brain, it causes epilepsy, a common occurrence in many developing countries.

A more devastating infection, though, is caused by oncospheres in faeces from dogs that harbour a small tapeworm, *Echinococcus granulosus*. In their normal intermediate hosts, which may be sheep, cattle, or even horses, the hexacanth, after boring through the intestinal wall, is carried to the lungs or liver by the bloodstream. In these locations, an enormous fluid-filled cyst develops, sometimes up to 50 cm in diameter, which buds off hundreds of small invaginated tapeworm heads and even daughter cysts, which bud off many more heads. The whole structure is called a hydatid cyst (see Figure 7.3c). If a human is unfortunate enough to become infected from dog faeces, these cysts can occur in the same organs as in the natural intermediate host. The fluid in the cyst contains parasite antigens, so if it ruptures, the host is suddenly exposed to huge quantities of these antigens, to which it is strongly hypersensitive. In most cases, the host suffers anaphylactic shock and death (the process is explained in Book 3, via the Immunology CD material).

7.5 Roundworms

Roundworms belong to the phylum Nematoda which is probably one of the most abundant groups of organisms on Earth. They include many free-living members and, as parasites, they invade almost every kind of animal and many plants. Unlike other helminths, roundworms may penetrate a variety of body tissues, and they have a long history as human parasites. We deal here with just two groups as examples: hookworms, which have direct life cycles; and filarial worms, which have indirect life cycles.

7.5.1 Hookworms

Human hookworms include two species, *Ancylostoma duodenale* and *Necator americanus*, which are worldwide in distribution in areas with moist, warm climates. Both species occur in Africa, Asia and the Americas, but *Ancylostoma* is also found in the Middle East and Southern Europe. The adult worms live attached, by means of ferocious-looking mouth capsules (Figure 7.17 overleaf), to the intestinal mucosa, from which they suck blood. This results in chronic blood loss and gradual depletion of the body's iron stores, leading to anaemia. According to WHO, one billion people worldwide are infected with hookworms. Although direct mortality is relatively low (about 7000 deaths per year), the exhaustion and vulnerability to infection resulting from hookworm-related anaemia significantly reduces the lifespan, particularly of children.

The hookworm life cycle follows the pattern in Figure 7.1c, eggs being passed in faeces to develop in moist, warm soil to a third larval stage. These larvae can survive in the environment for about four weeks, but in contact with human skin they penetrate into a blood vessel and are carried via the heart to the lungs, where they emerge into the pulmonary cavity. They ascend the bronchi by the mucociliary escalator and are swallowed to eventually end up in the intestine.

An interesting feature of hookworm infection is the pattern of infectivity exhibited in susceptible communities.

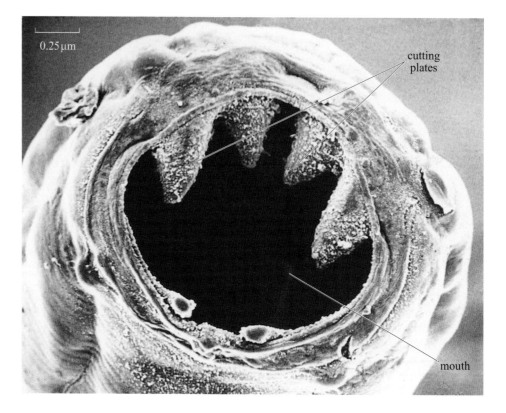

FIGURE 7.17
Scanning electron micrograph of the oral opening of *Ancylostoma duodenale*, a species of human hookworm. Note the presence of four cutting 'teeth', two on each side.

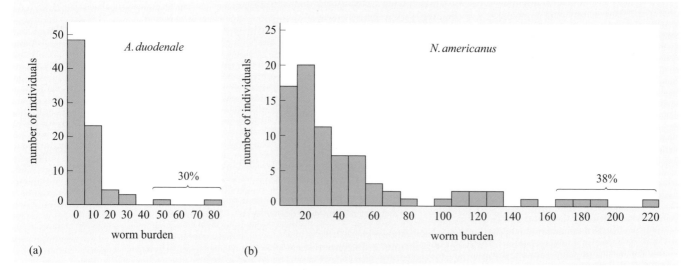

FIGURE 7.18 The frequency distribution of infection with (a) *Ancylostoma duodenale* and (b) *Necator americanus* in Kargar Malleh Village, Iran. The number of worms present inside the host is referred to as the 'worm burden'. (see Croll and Ghadirian 1980).

Examine Figure 7.18.

○ What is the most striking feature of the distribution of hookworms among infected individuals?

● In *A. duodenale* two persons carry about 30% of all the worms; in *N. americanus* four persons carry about 38% of all worms found.

○ Can you think of any reason for this 'clumped' (also referred to as 'overdispersed') distribution?

● Some individuals may just be more susceptible to infection.

Variations in immunity could be an explanation for this overdispersal, but Schad and Anderson (1985) have suggested that heavily infected individuals are predisposed by some undefined genetic, ecological, behavioural or social factors. In fact, human hookworms survive an extremely immunologically hostile environment, given that they are constantly taking in blood containing host antibodies. Pritchard (1995) has identified a number of protective molecules that may help them evade the immune response of the host.

7.5.2 Filarial worms

Filariasis is caused by roundworms that inhabit the lymphatic vessels and subcutaneous tissues. Three species are responsible for much of the morbidity due to the disease: *Wucheraria bancrofti* (most tropical areas) and *Brugia malayi* (Asia), which cause lymphatic filariasis; and *Onchocerca volvulus* (Africa, Middle East), which causes river blindness.

Figure 7.19 shows the general life cycle of these parasites.

○ What are the main differences between this cycle and that of hookworms?

● 1 A vector is involved to transfer the larval worm from host to host.

2 Although in both life cycles the infective stage is the third stage larva, here a fourth stage develops into the adult.

3 There is no free-living larval form.

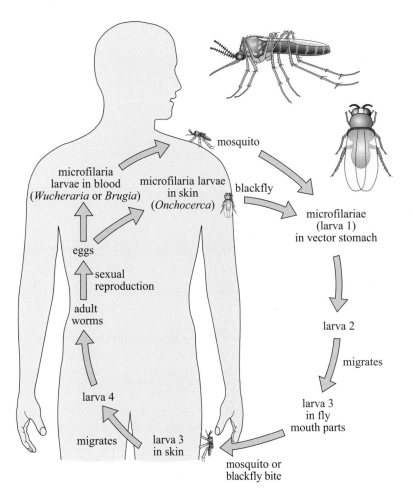

FIGURE 7.19
The life cycle of filarial roundworms. These parasites spend 10–14 days in the insect vector and 3–12 months in the human host.

mosquito

microfilaria larvae in blood (*Wucheraria* or *Brugia*)

microfilaria larvae in skin (*Onchocerca*)

blackfly

microfilariae (larva 1) in vector stomach

eggs

sexual reproduction

adult worms

larva 2

migrates

larva 4

migrates

larva 3 in skin

larva 3 in fly mouth parts

mosquito or blackfly bite

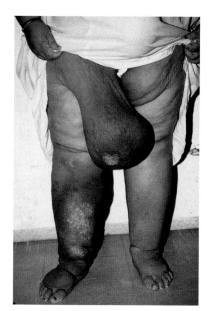

FIGURE 7.20
Elephantiasis of the lower limbs and body tissue caused by filariasis.

Human filariasis is a chronic and debilitating disease that causes extensive morbidity but little mortality. In lymphatic filariasis, the most dramatic symptom is caused by the blockage of the lymphatic system by the adult worm, resulting in the condition known as elephantiasis (Figure 7.20) where lower limbs, and often genitals, can swell grotesquely.

Adult *Onchocerca* worms occur in nodules in subcutaneous tissue, but most of the symptoms of onchocerciasis are caused by the microfilaria larvae, which can cause inflammation of the outer layers of the skin, resulting in intense itching. If the larvae invade the cornea, iris or optic nerves, they can cause blindness, and this happens in about 5–8% of all cases. As the vector is the blackfly (*Simulium*), which breeds in fast-running rivers in tropical Africa, this severe symptom is termed 'river blindness'.

One other important roundworm, which has been the subject of a WHO eradication programme, is *Dracunculus medinensis* (guinea worm), a large worm that is found under the skin, where it forms blisters. When the blisters burst, larvae are released into water where they enter small crustaceans and go on to mature into infective-stage larvae. These infect new hosts through drinking water, migrating eventually to the skin where they mature into the adult worm. We will return to a study of the public health implications of this parasite in Book 7.

7.6 Hosts and parasites – an evolutionary perspective

Until around the mid-20th century a central axiom of textbooks on parasites was that a well adapted parasite would have little effect on its host. It was assumed that natural selection would drive the evolution of the host–parasite relationship to one of a stable coexistence. However, if a successful parasite is one that exploits its host for its own nutritional needs, it is more likely that natural selection would favour the parasites that were more successful at extracting nutrients, and that such adaptations would be carried by their offspring. Thus, such evolutionary adaptation is likely to result in more, rather than less, harm to the host (Anderson and May, 1982). In addition, an analysis of the relationship between stress and parasitism by Esch *et al.* (1975) indicated that host susceptibility to parasite infection increases when the host becomes physiologically stressed. As it is likely that the very event of parasitic infection would increase stress, hosts may thus be more susceptible to further infection. So far, this argument only reflects what might happen, through natural selection, to the parasite. But what of the host?

○ In what ways do you think that natural selection would drive host adaptations that reduce the effects of parasitic infection?

● By increasing the effectiveness of its immune system.

Natural selection would favour the survival of, and the production of viable offspring by, those hosts that, by chance, possessed a more effective immune response. Thus, far from a balanced coexistence between host and parasite, there is often a kind of evolutionary 'arms race' between them. Such an idea is reflected by the 'Red Queen' hypothesis. (This hypothesis derives its name from Lewis Carroll's book *Through the Looking Glass*, where the Red Queen tells Alice to run faster and faster to stay on the same spot.) The parasite-versus-host arms race may be rather subtle in its effects. For example, some parasites may adapt to be more virulent, reduce host mobility or even kill the host, whereas others may adapt to have less virulence, so that they survive in the host for some time.

▢ From the life cycles you studied earlier, can you suggest a benefit for either of these strategies?

⬤ Life cycles that depend on the definitive host being infected by a cyst stage, such as in tapeworms, would be enhanced by the easy capture and consumption of the intermediate host by predators. Those that depend on the continual release of an infective stage, such as schistosome cercariae, would benefit from the prolonged survival of the snail intermediate host. In most cases, the long survival of the definitive host enhances continued egg release from the mature parasite.

For a population of hosts to 'compete' in this arms race, constant mutation of genotypes to create variation in the immune system is necessary to counter mutational changes in the parasites' defence mechanisms.

▢ Which reproductive process would increase genetic variation in a host population?

⬤ Sexual reproduction.

It is thus very possible that sexual reproduction evolved in organisms as an adaptive response to infection by parasites. We will consider a more detailed analysis of the concept of coevolution in Book 5.

7.7 Conclusions

In this chapter we have examined some of the important diseases of humans caused by 'worms'. The eradication of many of these infections, which cause such misery throughout large parts of the world, involves the expenditure of much resource, in terms of both research time and money, and a thorough understanding of the biology of the parasites is essential to these procedures. However, the task of eradication, or even control, is tremendously difficult and can be affected by many environmental, economic, social and scientific factors.

There is no doubt that eradication of these diseases is very important, but would we really want to be entirely free of parasitic infections? The answer is probably 'no', since the stimulation of our immune system may depend on coevolution with our parasites. It is possible that the increase of allergic illnesses and autoimmune diseases, more prevalent in the Western world than the developing world, may be a result of our immune systems responding in different ways, when not challenged by parasites early in life. Thus, coexistence as well as coevolution with our parasites may be essential for health and survival.

Summary of Chapter 7

1   Parasitic 'worms' belonging to the phyla Platyhelminthes (flukes and tapeworms) and Nematoda (roundworms) are worldwide in distribution, but are particularly prevalent in developing countries.

2   Parasite life cycles include a number of larval stages, which enhance transmission from host to host, either directly or indirectly by means of intermediate hosts or vectors.

3   Schistosomiasis (blood fluke disease) is a major disease, adult flukes infecting blood vessels around the intestine or bladder, depending on the species.

4   Other flukes may occur in the liver or lungs.

5   Tapeworms in the gut are less debilitating, but sometimes larval stages in the tissues may cause severe disease symptoms.

6   Roundworms are worldwide in distribution, both adult and larvae being responsible for disease symptoms.

7   Parasites and hosts appear to show coevolution.

Learning outcomes for Chapter 7

When you have studied this chapter, you should be able to:

7.1   Define and use, or recognize definitions and applications of, each of the terms printed in **bold** in the text. (*all Section 7 questions*)

7.2   Appreciate the worldwide distribution of invertebrate parasites of humans and some of the reasons that explain such a distribution. (*Question 7.2*)

7.3   Understand the biology of the life cycles of flukes, tapeworms and roundworms, and suggest methods of control and prevention. (*Question 7.1 and 7.3*)

Questions for Chapter 7

Question 7.1

Briefly explain the difference between the terms 'definitive host' and 'intermediate host' in the life cycle of parasitic worms.

Question 7.2

In the city of Rio de Janeiro, a hypothetical common invertebrate parasite, whose definitive host is human, has an intermediate host that lives in freshwater ponds. Investigations show that people living at the bottom of the nearby Sugarloaf mountain are ten times more likely to be infested with the worm than people living 500 m up the mountain. Suggest two reasons why this might be so.

Question 7.3

Figure 7.21 outlines the life cycle of a theoretical parasitic fluke of humans.

(a) List all the possible larval stages that may occur between A and B, B and C, and C and A.

(b) Indicate where, and by what means, measures might be applied to exert control and/or prevention of the transmission of this parasite from one human host to another.

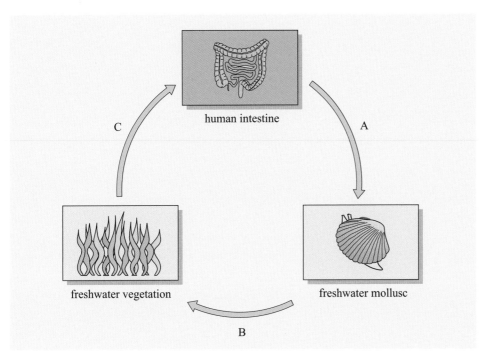

FIGURE 7.21
Life cycle of a theoretical parasitic fluke.

8 DISEASES WITH AN UNEXPECTED AETIOLOGY

The aetiology of a disease means its underlying *causes*, but it can also refer to the *study* of the causes of disease. This is a short chapter in which we describe two diseases that have unexpectedly been found to be caused by specific pathogens. In fact, these two cases are now well documented, but there is little doubt that many more diseases, currently not thought to be infectious, will turn out to be caused by pathogens.

8.1 *Helicobacter*

In 1982, in Perth, Australia, Dr Barry Marshall drank a culture of the Gram-negative spiral bacterium *Helicobacter pylori*. You met this bacterium back in Chapter 1 (Section 1.2.3), where it was described as being particularly well adapted to survive in the human stomach. A week after drinking the culture, Marshall developed gastritis, or inflammation of the epithelium lining the stomach. By using himself rather drastically as experimental material, he attempted to convince the scientific establishment that gastritis and both peptic and duodenal ulcers could have an infectious cause, and not simply be the result of too much stress and spicy food. Marshall's suggestion that microbes might be responsible was an unexpected explanation for the aetiology of these conditions.

The story began for Marshall in the late 1970s, when a curved bacterium was repeatedly isolated from gut tissue samples taken from ulcer patients (see Figure 8.1). A possible identity for this microbe was *Helicobacter pylori*, which frequently has a curved appearance (Figure 8.2). When the ulcer patients, and others with the related condition of gastritis, were treated with an antibiotic, their condition improved. Further investigations found the curved bacillus to be present in all samples from patients with duodenal ulcers and 80% of those with peptic ulcers. In spite of these results showing close compliance with Koch's postulates, it took until the mid-1990s for the idea that these diseases were infectious to become widely accepted by the medical and scientific establishments. *H. pylori* is now known to be responsible for most cases of gastritis where there is no other primary cause, and to produce almost all gastric and duodenal ulcers. It has also been linked with some types of stomach cancer. Ulcer patients have been freed from years of taking anti-ulcer drugs containing cimetidine, such as Tagamet and Zantac, in favour of a one-off course of antibiotics.

However, the *Helicobacter pylori* story may not be as clear-cut as it seems. Evidence is coming to light that suggests that *H. pylori* is not a pathogen, but a commensal that protects its host from diarrhoea and a rare type of cancer. The whole story promises to be as convoluted as the bacterium itself.

8.2 Cervical cancer

Cervical cancer, or cancer of the neck of the womb, has long been known to medicine. The fact that it is an important infectious disease, however, has only been established since the 1980s. Before then, a patient with cervical cancer was

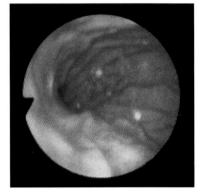
(a)

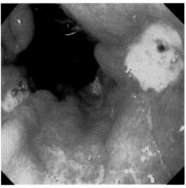
(b)

FIGURE 8.1
Appearance of (a) the interior of a normal stomach and (b) a gastric ulcer (upper right), seen by endoscopy.

10 μm

FIGURE 8.2
Helicobacter pylori on the gastric mucosa of a patient with gastritis.

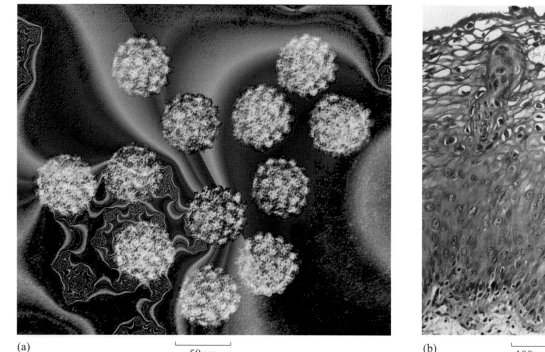

(a)

50 nm

(b)

100 μm

FIGURE 8.3
(a) Human papilloma virus (HPV) particles. (b) Appearance of the cervical epithelium after infection with HPV. Note that the cells appear disorganized, and the normal horizontal layering has been lost.

considered to have just been 'unlucky'. The turn-around began when a virus was found to be associated with warts, or papillomas, which are non-cancerous tumours that grow on the skin and genitals and in the mouth. Similar viruses had been found in animals, where they were associated with the development of cancer. By the late 1970s, it was being suggested that the human papilloma virus (HPV) might be associated with certain human cancers. Further investigations showed that there was not just one, but many types of HPV, and by the 1980s they were established as a major cause of cervical cancer (Figure 8.3). Around 95% of invasive cervical cancers contain HPV DNA, but this DNA comes from only a few types of HPV, most notably HPV 16 and 18. Genital HPVs are mainly transmitted from person to person during sexual intercourse, which means that simple precautions such as using a condom can do much to protect individuals from infection. Cervical cancer, the second most common cancer to affect women, can now be prevented altogether, as well as being detected with a smear test and successfully cured.

8.3 Atherosclerosis

The infectious natures of peptic ulcers and cervical cancer are now well established, but that isn't the case for the next disease we consider, atherosclerosis. Atherosclerosis is the build-up of fatty deposits on arterial walls (see Figure 8.4), leading to narrowing of the arteries, and is the chief cause of coronary heart disease. In 1993, a Finnish study found that 70% of the heart attack patients sampled had evidence of infection with the bacterium *Chlamydia pneumoniae*. This bacterium, as its name suggests, is known for causing a type of pneumonia and belongs to the same genus as *Chlamydia trachomatis*, which you have already met (Section 2.6.3). The level of *C. pneumoniae* infection observed in the heart attack patients was significantly higher than that observed for the control group. Since the heart attack patients had no recent history of pneumonia, it was suggested that chronic infection with *C. pneumoniae* might be a risk factor for atherosclerosis. Interestingly, *C. pneumoniae* bacteria have been found in fatty plaques removed from arteries with atherosclerosis (see Figure 8.5). What if *C. pneumoniae* infection is the *cause* of atherosclerosis? This disease, which is a major killer in industrialized nations, would then be seen as a modern plague. As yet, the role of *C. pneumoniae* in atherosclerosis has not been fully defined, but the possibilities in this area are very interesting.

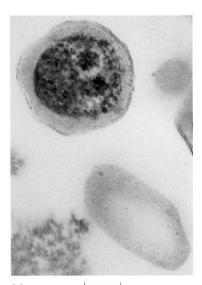

(a)   300 nm

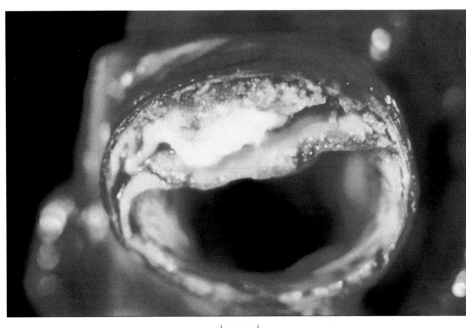

0.5 mm

FIGURE 8.4 Transverse section through a coronary artery, showing a large plaque and fatty deposits around the arterial wall.

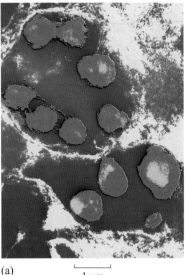

(a)   1 μm

FIGURE 8.5
Chlamydia pneumoniae and atherosclerotic plaques. (a) *Chlamydia pneumoniae* seen by coloured transmission electron micrograph. (b) Coloured transmission electron micrograph through an area of plaque in a coronary artery. The pear-shaped structures in red are thought to be *C. pneumoniae*. They lie within so-called foam cells, fat-filled cells that are a major component of plaques.

8.4 What about the future?

We turn now to some tantalizing evidence that may one day help us to understand two of our most feared diseases: Alzheimer's and schizophrenia. In 1998, an American study reported that *C. pneumoniae* had been found in 22 out of 23 brains from Alzheimer's patients, but in only one out of 25 control brains that were examined (Balin *et al.*, 1998). Similarly, workers studying schizophrenia found the protoctist parasite *Toxoplasma gondii* (Section 5.5.1) more commonly in schizophrenic patients than in controls. *T. gondii* is known to infect the human brain, so could schizophrenia be another manifestation of toxoplasmosis, and Alzheimer's the result of a *C. pneumoniae* infection? At the other end of the lifespan, a recent report implicates an *E. coli* exotoxin in sudden infant death syndrome (SIDS). The notion that SIDS has a bacterial aetiology is not new, but for the first time the toxin has been found in the blood of 68 babies who died of SIDS, but in none of 60 healthy control babies or 17 control babies who died of other causes (Goldwater, 2002).

All of the obvious infectious diseases have now been described, which leaves us the diseases where microbes could be the cause, but are not yet clearly apparent. Searching for these 'hidden' infections may yet unlock the secrets to our deadliest and most feared diseases. We cannot know the future of the study of infectious disease, but one thing is certain – it will be an exciting one.

Summary of Chapter 8

1　Several gastric diseases are now thought to be due to *Helicobacter pylori*.

2　Cervical cancer is now believed to be due to infection with particular strains of human papilloma virus.

3　There is a possibility that other diseases, including atherosclerosis, Alzheimer's and schizophrenia, have an infection as a contribution to their multifactorial aetiology.

Learning outcomes for Chapter 8

When you have studied this chapter, you should be able to:

8.1　Define and use, or recognize definitions and applications of, each of the terms printed in **bold** in the text. (*Questions 8.1 and 8.2*)

8.2　Outline the evidence that peptic and duodenal ulcers are due to *Helicobacter* infection. (*Question 8.1*)

8.3　Briefly describe the evidence that cervical cancer is caused by HPV infection. (*Question 8.2*)

8.4　Summarize the evidence that suggests that Alzheimer's disease and schizophrenia may have infectious aetiologies. (*Question 8.2*)

Questions for Chapter 8

Question 8.1

Suggest a reason why the medical profession was reluctant to accept a microbial aetiology for peptic and duodenal ulcers.

Question 8.2

To what extent does evidence exist suggesting a microbial aetiology for (a) cervical cancer and (b) schizophrenia? What other explanation might there be for the observed distribution of *T. gondii*?

REFERENCES

Anderson, R. M., and May, R. M. (1982) Co-evolution of hosts and parasites, *Parasitology*, **85**, pp. 411–426.

Balin *et al.* (1998) as described in Ewald, P. W. (2000) *Plague Time*, Free Press, New York, p. 125.

Bartlett, J. G. (1996) *Pocket Book of Infectious Disease Therapy*, Williams and Wilkins, London.

Croll, N. A. and Ghadirian, E. (1980) Wormy persons: contributions to the nature and patterns of overdispersion with *Ascaris lumbricoides, Ancylostoma duodenale, Necator americanus* and *Trichuris trichiura, Tropical and Geographical Medicine*, **33**, pp. 241–248.

Curio, E. (1988) Behaviour and parasitism, in *Parasitology in Focus*, H. Melhorn (ed.), New York: Springer-Verlag, pp. 149–160.

Esch, G. W., Gibbons, J. W. and Bourke, J. E. (1975) An analysis of the relationship between stress and parasites, *American Midlands Naturalist*, **93**, pp. 339–353.

Goldwater, P. (2002) as reported in Clayton, J., Blood toxin implicated in SIDS, *BioMedNet News*, 25 April 2002.

Mata, L. (1982) Sociocultural factors in the control and prevention of parasitic diseases, *Review of Infectious Diseases*, **4**, pp. 871–819.

Pritchard, D. (1995) The survival strategies of hookworms, *Parasitology Today*, **11**, pp. 255–259.

Rollinson, D. and Johnston, D. A. (1996) Schistosomiasis: A persistent parasitic disease. *Interdisciplinary Science Reviews*, **21**(2), pp. 140–154.

Rollinson, D. and Johnston, D. A. (1999) Genome analysis: Helping to solve the molecular mysteries of schistosomes, *Helminthologia*, **36**(3), pp. 147–158.

Schad, G. A. and Anderson, R. M. (1985) Predisposition to hookworm infection in humans *Science*, **228**, pp. 1537–1539.

Taylor, L. H., Latham, S. M. and Woolhouse, M. E. J. (2001) Risk factors for human disease emergence, *Philosophical Transactions of the Royal Society London, B*, **356**(1411), pp. 983–989.

FURTHER SOURCES

Broda, P. (1979) *Plasmids*, W. H. Freeman, Oxford.

Brown, T. A. (1996) *Gene Cloning* (3rd edn), Chapman and Hall, London.

Brown, T. A. (1996) *Genetics: A Molecular Approach* (2nd edn), Chapman and Hall, London.

Ewald, P. W. (2000) *Plague Time*, Free Press, New York.

Flint, S. J., Enquist, L. W., Krug, R. M., Racaniello, V. R. and Skalka, A. M. (2000) *Principles of Virology*, ASM Press, Washington, DC.

Fullick, A. (2000) *Biology*, Heinemann, Oxford.

Garrett, L. (1995) *The Coming Plague*, Penguin Books, London.

Gillin, F. D. and Reiner, D. S. (1996) Cell biology of the primitive eukaryote *Giardia lamblia*, *Annual Review of Microbiology*, **50**, pp. 679–705.

Greenwood, D., Slack, R. and Peutherer, J. (eds) (2000) *Medical Microbiology* (15th edn), Churchill Livingstone, London.

Groisman, E. A. (ed.) (2001) *Principles of Bacterial Pathogenesis*, Academic Press, London.

Hamilton, G. (2001) Dead man walking, *New Scientist*, **2303** (August), pp. 31–33.

Heritage, J., Evans, E. G. V. and Killington, R. A. (1996) *Introductory Microbiology*, Cambridge University Press, Cambridge.

Heritage, J., Evans, E. G. V. and Killington, R. A. (1999) *Microbiology in Action*, Cambridge University Press, Cambridge.

Jones, P. (2001) Smart proteins, Inside Science: Life sciences, *New Scientist*, **2282** (17 March).

Krause, R. M. (ed.) (2000) *Emerging Infections*, Academic Press, London.

MacQueen, H. (2001) (ed.) S204 Biology: Uniformity and Diversity, Book 4 *Microbes*, The Open University, Milton Keynes.

Miller, R. L., Armelagos, G. J., Ikram, S., DeJong, N., Kriger, F. W. and Deelder, A. M. (1992) Palaeoepidemiology of *Schistosoma* infection in mummies, *British Medical Journal*, **304**, pp. 555–556.

Mims, C. A., Nash, A. and Stephen, J. (2001) *Mims' Pathogenesis of Infectious Disease* (5th edn), Academic Press, London.

Olds, R. J. (1975) *A Colour Atlas of Microbiology*, Wolfe Medical Books, London.

Ornston, L. N. and Balows, A. (eds) (2000) *Annual Review of Microbiology*, **54**, Annual Reviews, Palo Alto, California..

Prescott, L. M., Harley, J. P. and Klein, D. A. (1999) *Microbiology* (4th edn), WCB McGraw-Hill, London.

Ridge, I. (2001) (ed.) S204 Biology: Uniformity and Diversity, Book 5 *Plants*, The Open University, Milton Keynes.

Ridge, I. and Pond, C. M (2001) (eds) S204 Biology: Uniformity and Diversity, Book 1 *Introduction to Diversity*, The Open University, Milton Keynes.

Roberts, M. B. V. (1980) *Biology: A Functional Approach*, Nelson, Surrey.

Saffrey, J. and Stewart, M. (1997) (eds) SK220 Human Biology and Health, Book 3 *Maintaining the Whole*, The Open University, Milton Keynes.

Stanier, R. Y., Ingraham, J. L., Wheelis, M. L. and Painter, P. R. (1987) *General Microbiology* (5th edn), MacMillan Education, London.

Vines, A. E. and Rees, N. (1982) *Plant and Animal Biology*, Vol. 1, Pitman Press, Bath.

Wilson, J. D., Braunwald, E., Isselbacher, K. J. *et al.* (1991) *Harrison's Principles of Internal Medicine*, International edition (12th edn), McGraw-Hill, New York.

ANSWERS TO QUESTIONS

QUESTION 1.1

You have encountered varying numbers of disease-causing agents in the categories given in the table below. Here we give several examples, but the list is not exhaustive and you may have come up with others.

Pathogen group	Example of disease
prion	BSE
virus	influenza, common cold, rubella, foot-and-mouth disease
bacterium	anthrax, cholera, syphilis, plague, food poisoning
fungus	thrush
protoctist	malaria, toxoplasmosis
helminth	guinea worm, tapeworm

QUESTION 1.2

The main routes of infection and the corresponding first-line host defences are tabulated below.

Infection route	Host defences
skin	impermeable keratinous layer, fatty acids, low pH, sweat containing lysozyme and antibodies
respiratory	mucociliary escalator and the cough reflex
gastrointestinal	mucus, low pH in the stomach, vomiting and diarrhoea
genitourinary	flushing with urine and mucus, lining of cilia, low pH (females), antimicrobial prostate secretions (males)

In addition, all routes involve competition with commensals.

QUESTION 1.3

Both bacteria and helminths gain access to the gut by contaminated food or water. Both must be able to survive exposure to stomach acid. Bacteria are adapted to acidic conditions, and some, like *Helicobacter*, cannot live at higher pH levels. Helminths are able to pass through the stomach into the intestine as resistant cysts. Once in the intestine, both types of pathogen must anchor themselves to the gut mucosa to avoid being swept away. Bacteria do this by adherent molecules and structures such as pili. Helminths attach via hooks or suckers.

QUESTION 2.1

Genus	Plural form
Bordetella	bordetellae
Borrelia	borreliae
Clostridium	clostridia
Corynebacterium	corynebacteria
Neisseria	neisseriae
Salmonella	salmonellae
Shigella	shigellae
Yersinia	yersiniae

QUESTION 2.2

Feature	Gram-positive	Gram-negative
peptidoglycan	thick; 20–80 nm	thin; 2–7 nm
membranes	plasma (cytoplasmic) membrane only	plasma membrane + outer membrane
teichoic acid	present	absent
lipid A	absent	present
lipopolysaccharide	absent	replaces phospholipids in outer membrane

QUESTION 2.3

Antibiotics are generally directed at either surface components or cellular metabolism. Bacteria, viruses and fungi generally have very different surface molecules (although, as you will learn in Book 3, their molecules may contain common structural elements). Bacteria are prokaryotes and fungi eukaryotes, so their metabolic processes show major differences; viruses have no metabolism of their own, but hijack that of their hosts. Therefore agents that can combat all these types of pathogen, without also damaging the patient, are rare.

QUESTION 2.4

There are three main substances that are found only in the cell walls of acid-fast mycobacteria and so could be targets for selective toxicity:

1   Arabinogalactan, the branched polymer made of alternating arabinose and galactose residues, which is just outside the peptidoglycan layer.

2   Mycolic acid, the long-chain fatty acid that gives the bacteria a waxy coating and is covalently attached to the arabinogalactan.

3   Lipo-arabinomannan and the other glycolipids that forms the outermost layer of the mycobacterial cell.

Any of these three mycobacterial cell wall components could be targets for antimycobacterial drugs.

QUESTION 2.5

Doderlein's bacillus is a commensal species that lives in the vagina of women of reproductive age. The bacillus metabolizes glycogen in the vaginal epithelial cells, producing lactic acid. This reduces the vaginal pH to around 5.0, which is too low for many other species, including many pathogens. If antibiotic treatment kills the Doderlein's bacilli, the vaginal pH rises, allowing opportunistic or exogenous infections to take hold.

QUESTION 2.6

The two classes of microbial toxin are endotoxins and exotoxins. Endotoxins are components of the bacterial surface, and the most well-known is lipopolysaccharide, LPS. This works by stimulating the host's immune system to produce fever and endotoxic shock. Exotoxins are (usually) proteins secreted by pathogens that can cause symptoms even in the absence of the pathogen itself. Exotoxins have a variety of actions: they may bind to host cell surface receptors, initiating signalling pathways (cholera toxin affects ion channels); they may disrupt host cell membranes (pertussis cytotoxin kills ciliated epithelial cells); or they may target intracellular components (diptheria toxin interferes with protein synthesis). You may have used different examples.

QUESTION 2.7

Virulence factors are factors that assist pathogens in the infective process. They are generally encoded in pathogenicity islands. They act in mediating attachment of pathogen to host (adhesins, pili or fimbriae, capsules), in aiding pathogen nutrition (siderophores), or in facilitating pathogen spread (flagella, toxins, degradative enzymes).

QUESTION 2.8

The stages of the infection process are: gaining entry to the host, adherence to an appropriate site in the host, and growth, multiplication and spread.

QUESTION 2.9

Yersinia is transmitted by an insect bite or via the air as pneumonic plague; *Staphylococcus* enters via broken skin; *Corynebacterium* is an airborne respiratory pathogen; *Neisseria* is sexually transmitted; *Salmonella* is a gut pathogen that is transmitted by infected food and water; *E. coli* can be food-borne, but may also be a commensal that becomes an opportunistic pathogen.

QUESTION 2.10

New diseases can arise through mutation of an existing human pathogen to give a different set of symptoms, via mutation of an animal pathogen such that it can now infect humans, or by some shift in ecological balance such that humans become more exposed or susceptible to previously rare pathogens.

QUESTION 3.1

The porcelain bacterial filter and the electron microscope.

QUESTION 3.2

Viral genomes can be DNA or RNA, whereas bacterial genomes are only DNA; viral genomes can be single-stranded and segmented, whereas bacterial genomes are double-stranded and each piece can replicate by itself.

QUESTION 3.3

Advantage: all known viruses fall clearly into a discrete class.

Disadvantage: a virus cannot be classified merely by observation (e.g. by capsid shape); it must be studied to ascertain its replication strategy.

QUESTION 3.4

Both variola major and adenovirus are DNA viruses. Variola major replicates and is assembled entirely in the cytoplasm. It carries its own DNA-dependent RNA polymerase in the nucleosome. New virions acquire an envelope from the host cell membrane, and may be released without lysing the cell. On the other hand, adenovirus is replicated and assembled entirely in the nucleus. New virions lie in clusters forming paracrystalline arrays. These arrays may become so big as to cause damage to host chromosomes.

QUESTION 3.5

(a) The main cytopathic effects are: changes in appearance, such as rounding up or syncytium formation; the formation of inclusion bodies; membrane damage; triggering of apoptosis; and transformation. (b) Membrane damage and triggering of apoptosis are commonly seen with cytocidal viral infections.

QUESTION 3.6

(a) A, C and D are symptoms of measles; (b) B and E are symptoms of smallpox.

QUESTION 3.7

A haemorrhagic fever is a usually fatal fever that starts with headache and muscle pain, then progresses to local and systemic haemorrhage. This haemorrhaging leads to circulatory shock (massive loss of blood volume), and this is what kills the patient. The Ebola virus is a recently emerged virus that causes haemorrhagic fever.

QUESTION 3.8

A bacteriophage is a virus that infects bacteria. There are cytocidal and non-cytocidal phages, and the cytocidal ones could be used therapeutically. The idea is that phages could be used to destroy bacteria that are resistant to antibiotics. The phages would be introduced into the patient by topical application, injection, inhalation or by mouth, as appropriate, and would seek out and destroy the pathogenic bacteria without affecting the host (selective toxicity). There has been only limited success so far with this approach.

QUESTION 4.1

To determine whether MDD is a TSE, you would need to examine the brains of affected dogs microscopically to see whether changes consistent with a TSE were occurring. Next, you would need to rule out the involvement of more conventional pathogens. You would probably look for non-canine nucleic acid in the affected animals. It is likely that you would find plenty; the crucial test is whether you find nucleic acid from the same pathogen in all the affected dogs (Koch's postulates). If this failed, you would begin a search for a protein molecule closely resembling a canine neuron membrane glycoprotein, that was insoluble in mild detergents and resistant to Proteinase K. If you found such a molecule, you would test your hypothesis by injecting it into healthy dogs and seeing if they developed MDD. If they did, this would be strong evidence that MDD is a TSE caused by a prion.

QUESTION 4.2

As in the cases of scrapie and BSE, the industrial processes involved in rendering carcases and preparing animal feed from them are insufficient to destroy prions. Therefore if MDD-infected dog carcases were fed to other dogs, many more MDD cases might be expected to appear. Dogs have a fairly short lifespan, and TSEs are generally slow diseases, but quicker onsets are possible, as with vCJD. Thus from an animal-welfare perspective you would probably advise the government not to allow this recycling process.

However, governments are pragmatic, and may consider that there is no danger to humans, as dogs do not often (in the UK at least) enter the human food chain. You might counter this argument by pointing out that there remains a danger to people who handle the processed meat, including many dog owners who are also voters. Moreover, there are well documented cases when prions have unexpectedly arisen, such as in the original transmission of the mutant prion to cows. Events such as this are unpredictable, all the more so since prions are relatively poorly understood. In the circumstances, you would probably advise the government to legislate as quickly as possible against the use of infected carcases of any species in any food production system. Whether your advice would be heeded is another matter!

QUESTION 5.1

Toxoplasmosis: *Toxoplasma gondii*, an apicomplexan; giardiasis: *Giardia lamblia*, a flagellate; Chagas' disease: *Trypanosoma cruzi*, a flagellate; amoebic keratitis: *Acanthamoeba*, an amoeba.

QUESTION 5.2

DNA (yes), ATP synthesis (yes), thiol groups (yes), mitochondrial function (yes), ribosomes (yes), folic acid (yes).

QUESTION 5.3

Any three of: *Giardia lamblia*, *Entamoeba histolytica*, *Acanthamoeba*, *Toxoplasma gondii* (this transmission route is rare for *Toxoplasma*, but possible), *Cryptosporidium*.

QUESTION 6.1

The infection might be: (1) tinea pedis, acquired from another person; or (2) a ringworm infection acquired from a farm animal; or (3) a subcutaneous mycosis acquired from fungal spores in the soil.

QUESTION 6.2

Candida is a frequent commensal of the skin, mouth, gut and vagina. If the fungus is transferred to, and grows on, the penis, its feeding mechanism means that extracellular enzymes will be poured onto the tissue of the penis. This results in tissue breakdown and inflammation, and general redness and soreness.

QUESTION 7.1

The definitive host harbours the sexually mature stage of the parasite. The intermediate host harbours a series of different larval stages, which often undergo asexual reproduction, so increasing the chance of transmission to the definitive host.

QUESTION 7.2

The reasons could be biological or social. The prevalence of the secondary host may be lower at a higher altitude because of factors such as temperature, rainfall or rate of water evaporation. In Rio, people with more money tend to live further up Sugarloaf mountain than the poor, who live at the bottom. With more money comes better sanitation, cleaner water and living conditions, and better general health. Both these groups of factors could explain the observation.

QUESTION 7.3

(a) Between A and B: miracidium; between B and C: sporocyst, redia, cercaria, metacercaria; between C and A: metacercaria (this develops into the adult worm, which produces eggs which are released in the faeces into water).

(b) A: prevent human faeces from contaminating the water supply. B: attempt to kill the snail by the use of chemicals that kill molluscs, or introduce a predator of the snail. C: clear the vegetation, or avoid eating it. If it is eaten, clean and cook it properly.

QUESTION 8.1

Prior to the discovery of *H. pylori*, everyone had been fairly convinced of the role of stress, overeating and excessive drinking in promoting ulcers. Furthermore, when the evidence began to appear, an apparent weakness in the case for *H. pylori*'s role in the aetiology of ulcers was that the microbe could be detected in only some, and not all, clinical specimens. Even now, it is accepted that some ulcers are not due to *Helicobacter* infection.

QUESTION 8.2

(a) The evidence for a microbial aetiology for cervical cancer is very strong: 95% of cervical cancers contain DNA from HPV type 16 or 18. (b) The evidence for a microbial aetiology for schizophrenia is less strong at present. All that can be said is that *Toxoplasma gondii* is found more commonly in the brains of schizophrenic patients than in those of non-schizophrenic control subjects. It is possible that people with schizophrenia behave in ways that increase their exposure to *T. gondii*, or that their medication makes them more susceptible to infection.

ACKNOWLEDGEMENTS

Grateful acknowledgement is made to the following sources for permission to reproduce material in this book:

Chapter 1

Figure 1.1: Reprinted with permission from p. 102 of F. R. Moulton (1947), *Aerobiology*, Washington DC, American Association for the Advancement of Science.

Chapter 2

Figure 2.1: Schopf, J. W. and Blacic, J. M. (1971) 'New micro-organisms from the Bitter Springs Formation…', vol. **45**, *Journal of Paleontology*, The Paleontological Society; *Figure 2.7b*: Prescott, L., Harley, J. and Klein, D. (1999) 4th edn, *Microbiology*, copyright © The McGraw-Hill, reproduced with permission of The McGraw-Hill Companies, Inc.; *Figure 2.8*: Farrell, I. (1998) *Medical Microbiology*, 2nd edn, Mims, C. *et al.* (eds), Mosby International Limited; *Figure 2.10*: Arthur M. Siegelman/Visual Sun Limited; *Figures 2.11a, 2.12a, 2.27a*: Prescott *et al.* (1999) *Microbiology*, 4th edn, copyright © The McGraw-Hill, reproduced with permission of The McGraw-Hill Companies, Inc.; *Figures 2.14, 2.20*: From *A Colour Atlas of Microbiology*, R. J. Olds, Wolfe Medical Books; *Figure 2.15*: John D. Cunningham/Visual Sun Limited; *Figure 2.16*: George Musil/ Visual Sun Limited; *Figure 2.17*: Fred Hossier/Visual Sun Limited; *Figure 2.18*: Copyright © Rambo, W. M. (1998) *Medical Microbiology*, 2nd edn, Mims, C. *et al.* (eds), Mosby International Limited; *Figure 2.19*: Copyright © Franklin H. Top (2000) *Brock's Biology of Microorganisms*, 9th edn, Madigan, M. T. *et al.* (eds), Prentice Hall, Inc.; *Figure 2.21a*: By permission of Bruce Iverson; *Figure 2.21b*: David M. Philips/Visual Sun Limited; *Figures 2.22a, 2.22c*: Science Photo Library; *Figure 2.22b*: Dr P. Marazzi/Science Photo Library; *Figure 2.24*: Armed Forces Institute of Pathology; *Figure 2.25*: Dr Linda Stannard, UCT/Science Photo Library; *Figure 2.26*: Associated Press; *Figures 2.27b, 2.27c*: CDC/Peter Arnold Inc.

Chapter 3

Figures 3.1, 3.19: Mediscan; *Figure 3.2*: Reprinted from *Medical Microbiology*, 15th edn, Greenwood, D., Slack, R. C. B. and Peutherer, J. F. (eds), copyright © (1997) by permission of the publisher Churchill Livingstone; *Figure 3.3*: Finch, J. T. (2000) *Brock Biology of Microorganisms*, 9th edn, Madigan, M. T. *et al.* (eds), Prentice Hall, Inc.; *Figures 3.4c, 3.14*: Reprinted from *Medical Microbiology*, 15th edn, Greenwood, D., Slack, R. C. B. and Peutherer, J. F. (eds), copyright © (1997) by permission of the publisher Churchill Livingstone; *Figure 3.5a*: *Virology, Molecular Biology, Pathogenesis and Control*, S. J. Flint, ASM Press, Washington DC; *Figure 3.6a*: *Journal of Molecular Biology*; *Figures 3.8a, 3.11a*: Prescott, L. M. *et al.* (2002) *Microbiology*, 5th edn, The McGraw-Hill Companies, Inc.; *Figure 3.8b*: Dr D. W. Gregory, University of Aberden/Welcome Trust Medical Photographic Library; *Figures 3.10b, 3.11b, 3.17*: *Microbiology*, 4th edn, The McGraw-Hill Companies, Inc.; *Figure 3.18*: Stanley B. Burns, MD and The Burns Archive, New York/Science Photo Library.

Chapter 4

Figure 4.2: Dr Peter H. Gibson.

Chapter 5

Figure 5.1a: Professor P. M. Motta and F. M. Magliocca/Science Photo Library; *Figure 5.1b*: CNRI/Science Photo Library; *Figure 5.1c*: Reprinted from *Emerging Infections*, Krause, R. M., copyright © (1998) Academic Press. With permission from Elsevier Science; *Figure 5.2*: Martin Dohrn/Science Photo Library; *Figure 5.3a*: Juergen Berger, Max-Planck Institute/Science Photo Library; *Figure 5.4*: Science Photo Library; *Figure 5.5a*: T. M. Unit, Cornell University Medical College and Marsden, P. D./T. M. R./Welcome Photographic Library; *Figure 5.6*: Prescott, L. M., Harley, J. and Klein, D. A. (2002) *Microbiology*, 5th edn, The McGraw-Hill Companies, Inc.; *Figure 5.7a*: Courtesy of R. H. Gilman, from *Medical Microbiology*, 2nd edn, Mims, C. *et al.* (eds), 1998, Mosby International Limited; *Figure 5.7b*: Michael Abby/Science Photo Library; *Figure 5.8b*: *Medical Microbiology*, 3rd edn, P. R. Murray *et al.*, Mosby International Limited; *Figure 5.9a*: Moredun Animal Health/Science Photo Library; *Figure 5.9b*: Eye of Science/ Science Photo Library;

Chapter 6

Figures 6.1a, 6.1b: Murray *et al.*, from *Medical Microbiology*, 3rd edn, Mosby International Limited; *Figure 6.1c*: W. Ormerod. From *Brock's Biology of Microorganisms*, 9th edn, Prentice Hall, Inc.; *Figure 6.2a*: A. E. Prevost, from *Medical Microbiology*, 2nd edn, Mims, C. *et al.* (eds), 1998, Mosby International Limited; *Figure 6.2b*: M. J. Wood, from *Medical Microbiology*, 2nd edn, Mims, C. *et al.* (eds), 1998, Mosby International Limited; *Figure 6.2c*: M. H. Winterborn, from *Medical Microbiology*, Mims, C. *et al.* (eds), 1998, Mosby International Limited.

Chapter 7

Figure 7.4: Matthews, Bernard E. (1998) *An Introduction to Parasitology*, Cambridge University Press; *Figures 7.5, 7.6, 7.8a, 7.8b, 7.7, 7.9, 7.11, 7.13, 7.14*: The Welcome Trust; *Figure 7.18*: Croll, N. A. and Ghadirian, E. (1981) *Tropical and Geographical Medicine*, vol. **33**, pp. 241–248, Blackwell Science; *Figure 7.20*: Andy Crump/Science Photo Library.

Chapter 8

Figure 8.1a: Dr C. Liguory/CNRI/Science Photo Library; *Figure 8.1b*: David M. Martin, M.D./Science Photo Library; *Figure 8.2*: From *Medical Microbiology*, 2nd edn, Mims *et al.* (eds), 1998, Mosby International Limited; *Figure 8.3a*: Science Photo Library; *Figure 8.3b*: Dr Linda Stannard/UCT/Science Photo Library; *Figure 8.4*: BSIP VEN/Science Photo Library; *Figure 8.5a*: C. C. Kuo, University of Washington, Seattle/Science Photo Library; *Figure 8.5b*: Dr Kari Lounatmaa/ Science Photo Library.

Every effort has been made to trace all the copyright owners, but if any has been inadvertently overlooked, the publishers will be pleased to make the necessary arrangements at the first opportunity.

INDEX

Note: Entries in **bold** are key terms. Page numbers referring to information that is given only in a figure or caption are printed in *italics*.